MW00650986

www.EffortlessMath.com

... So Much More Online!

- ✓ FREE Math lessons

- ✓ More Math learning books!

- ✓ Mathematics Worksheets

- ✓ Online Math Tutors

Need a PDF version of this book?

Please visit www.EffortlessMath.com

Student Workbook for the MCAS Math Test

Complete coverage of all MCAS Math

topics + Practice Tests

By

Reza Nazari & Sam Mest

All inquiries should be addressed to:

info@effortlessMath.com

www.EffortlessMath.com

Published by: Effortless Math Education

www.EffortlessMath.com

Description

Student Workbook for the MCAS Math Test, which reflects the 2019 - 2020 test guidelines, provides students with the confidence and math skills they need to prepare for the MCAS Math test. It is designed to address the needs of MCAS test takers who must have a working knowledge of basic Math. Two full-length MCAS Math tests with detailed answers and explanations can help you discover your weak areas for concentrated study.

After completing this workbook, you will have solid foundation and adequate practice that is necessary to ace the MCAS Math test.

Student Workbook for the MCAS Math Test contains many exciting features to help you succeed on the MCAS Math test, including:

- Content 100% aligned with the 2019-2020 MCAS test
- Prepared by MCAS Math experts
- Complete coverage of all MCAS Math topics which you will need to ace the test
- Topics are grouped by category, so you can easily focus on the topics you struggle on
- 2 complete MCAS Math practice tests (featuring new question types) with detailed answers

This MCAS Math Workbook and other Effortless Math Education books are used by thousands of students each year to help them review core content areas, brush-up in math, discover their strengths and weaknesses, and achieve their best scores on the MCAS test.

Contents

Chapter 1:

Whole Numbers

Topics that you'll practice in this chapter:

✓ Rounding

✓ Whole Number Addition and Subtraction

✓ Whole Number Multiplication and Division

✓ Rounding and Estimates

Rounding

✏️ **Round each number to the nearest ten.**

1) 73 = ____   5) 37 = ____   9) 33 = ____

2) 46 = ____   6) 43 = ____   10) 77 = ____

3) 98 = ____   7) 19 = ____   11) 62 = ____

4) 31 = ____   8) 14 = ____   12) 49 = ____

✏️ **Round each number to the nearest hundred.**

13) 352 = ____   17) 732 = ____   21) 172 = ____

14) 921 = ____   18) 545 = ____   22) 215 = ____

15) 463 = ____   19) 785 = ____   23) 941 = ____

16) 345 = ____   20) 349 = ____   24) 833 = ____

✏️ **Round each number to the nearest thousand.**

25) 3,732 = ____   29) 9,840 = ____   33) 14,222 = ____

26) 5,498 = ____   30) 11,546 = ____   34) 30,700 = ____

27) 8,320 = ____   31) 21,505 = ____   35) 28,623 = ____

28) 18,240 = ____   32) 16,832 = ____   36) 17,950 = ____

Whole Number Addition and Subtraction

✎ **Find the sum or subtract.**

1)
$$
\begin{array}{r}
3,652 \\
-2,100 \\
\hline
\end{array}
$$

5)
$$
\begin{array}{r}
1,760 \\
+\ 543 \\
\hline
\end{array}
$$

9)
$$
\begin{array}{r}
4,330 \\
+2,541 \\
\hline
\end{array}
$$

2)
$$
\begin{array}{r}
5,250 \\
-3,432 \\
\hline
\end{array}
$$

6)
$$
\begin{array}{r}
6,520 \\
-3,730 \\
\hline
\end{array}
$$

10)
$$
\begin{array}{r}
7,629 \\
-\ 5,321 \\
\hline
\end{array}
$$

3)
$$
\begin{array}{r}
6,202 \\
-1,989 \\
\hline
\end{array}
$$

7)
$$
\begin{array}{r}
1,817 \\
+3,210 \\
\hline
\end{array}
$$

11)
$$
\begin{array}{r}
2,198 \\
+\ 6,985 \\
\hline
\end{array}
$$

4)
$$
\begin{array}{r}
5,396 \\
+1,401 \\
\hline
\end{array}
$$

8)
$$
\begin{array}{r}
5,333 \\
+1,005 \\
\hline
\end{array}
$$

12)
$$
\begin{array}{r}
8,961 \\
-6,895 \\
\hline
\end{array}
$$

✎ **Find the missing number.**

13) $1,210 + \underline{} = 3,420$

14) $2,835 - \underline{} = 1,568$

15) $\underline{} - 3,934 = 985$

16) $4,109 - 3,287 = \underline{}$

17) $5,432 + \underline{} = 6,009$

18) $4,950 - 3,410 = \underline{}$

Whole Number Multiplication and Division

✍ *Calculate each product.*

1)
$$
\begin{array}{r}
33 \\
\times\,42 \\
\hline
\end{array}
$$

3)
$$
\begin{array}{r}
62 \\
\times\,17 \\
\hline
\end{array}
$$

5)
$$
\begin{array}{r}
210 \\
\times\,23 \\
\hline
\end{array}
$$

2)
$$
\begin{array}{r}
59 \\
\times\,47 \\
\hline
\end{array}
$$

4)
$$
\begin{array}{r}
67 \\
\times\,39 \\
\hline
\end{array}
$$

6)
$$
\begin{array}{r}
145 \\
\times\,27 \\
\hline
\end{array}
$$

✍ *Find the missing quotient.*

7) $650 \div 25 = $ _____

8) $342 \div 19 = $ _____

9) $420 \div 6 = $ _____

10) $630 \div 9 = $ _____

11) $720 \div 15 = $ _____

12) $960 \div 20 = $ _____

13) $1750 \div 50 = $ _____

14) $4800 \div 80 = $ _____

15) $3200 \div 160 = $ _____

16) $560 \div 80 = $ _____

✍ *Solve each problem.*

17) $840 \div 7 = N$, $N = $ __

18) $1080 \div 12 = N$, $N = $ __

19) $N \div 13 = 9$, $N = $ __

20) $95 \times N = 1425$, $N = $ __

21) $780 \div N = 60$, $N = $ __

22) $N \times 16 = 256$, $N = $ __

Rounding and Estimates

✎ **Estimate the sum by rounding each number to the nearest ten.**

1) $28 + 65 = $ _____   5) $432 + 187 = $ _____

2) $72 + 39 = $ _____   6) $317 + 460 = $ _____

3) $81 + 56 = $ _____   7) $289 + 483 = $ _____

4) $61 + 23 = $ _____   8) $1523 + 982 = $ _____

✎ **Estimate the product by rounding each number to the nearest ten.**

9) $48 \times 22 = $ _____   13) $71 \times 91 = $ _____

10) $19 \times 34 = $ _____   14) $24 \times 47 = $ _____

11) $45 \times 62 = $ _____   15) $21 \times 53 = $ _____

12) $47 \times 28 = $ _____   16) $58 \times 82 = $ _____

✎ **Estimate the sum or product by rounding each number to the nearest ten.**

17)
$$\begin{array}{r} 41 \\ \times\ 23 \\ \hline \end{array}$$

19)
$$\begin{array}{r} 98 \\ +\ 38 \\ \hline \end{array}$$

21)
$$\begin{array}{r} 16 \\ \times\ 46 \\ \hline \end{array}$$

18)
$$\begin{array}{r} 73 \\ \times\ 13 \\ \hline \end{array}$$

20)
$$\begin{array}{r} 65 \\ +49 \\ \hline \end{array}$$

22)
$$\begin{array}{r} 77 \\ +\ 92 \\ \hline \end{array}$$

Answers

Rounding

1) 70	13) 400	25) 4,000
2) 50	14) 900	26) 5,000
3) 100	15) 500	27) 8,000
4) 30	16) 300	28) 18,000
5) 40	17) 700	29) 10,000
6) 40	18) 500	30) 12,000
7) 20	19) 800	31) 22,000
8) 10	20) 300	32) 17,000
9) 30	21) 200	33) 14,000
10) 80	22) 200	34) 31,000
11) 60	23) 900	35) 29,000
12) 50	24) 800	36) 18,000

Whole Number Addition and Subtraction

1) 1,552	7) 5,027	13) 2,210
2) 1,818	8) 6,338	14) 1,267
3) 4,213	9) 6,871	15) 4,919
4) 6,797	10) 2,308	16) 822
5) 2,303	11) 9,183	17) 577
6) 2,790	12) 2,066	18) 1,540

Whole Number Multiplication and Division

1) 1,386	9) 70	17) 120
2) 2,773	10) 70	18) 90
3) 1,054	11) 48	19) 117
4) 2,613	12) 48	20) 15
5) 4,830	13) 35	21) 13
6) 3,915	14) 60	22) 16
7) 26	15) 20	
8) 18	16) 7	

Rounding and Estimates

1) 90	9) 1,060	17) 940
2) 110	10) 650	18) 950
3) 140	11) 2,790	19) 140
4) 80	12) 1,320	20) 110
5) 620	13) 6,460	21) 740
6) 780	14) 1,130	22) 170
7) 770	15) 1,110	
8) 2510	16) 4,760	

Chapter 2:

Fractions and Decimals

Topics that you'll practice in this chapter:

✓ Simplifying Fractions

✓ Adding and Subtracting Fractions

✓ Multiplying and Dividing Fractions

✓ Adding and Subtract Mixed Numbers

✓ Multiplying and Dividing Mixed Numbers

✓ Adding and Subtracting Decimals

✓ Multiplying and Dividing Decimals

✓ Comparing Decimals

✓ Rounding Decimals

✓ Factoring Numbers

✓ Greatest Common Factor

✓ Least Common Multiple

Simplifying Fractions

🖎 *Simplify each fraction to its lowest terms.*

1) $\frac{30.}{54} =$

2) $\frac{24}{56} =$

3) $\frac{19}{228} =$

4) $\frac{36}{72} =$

5) $\frac{32}{80} =$

6) $\frac{15}{45} =$

7) $\frac{24}{60} =$

8) $\frac{8}{48} =$

9) $\frac{14}{84} =$

10) $\frac{65}{117} =$

11) $\frac{68}{102} =$

12) $\frac{39}{104} =$

13) $\frac{20}{65} =$

14) $\frac{14}{35} =$

15) $\frac{18}{40} =$

16) $\frac{25}{70} =$

17) $\frac{28}{49} =$

18) $\frac{22}{132} =$

19) $\frac{46}{69} =$

20) $\frac{48}{96} =$

21) $\frac{36}{90} =$

🖎 *Solve each problem.*

22) Which of the following fractions equal to $\frac{4}{7}$? _____

   A. $\frac{64}{100}$ B. $\frac{12}{108}$ C. $\frac{21}{105}$ D. $\frac{64}{112}$

23) Which of the following fractions equal to $\frac{7}{9}$? _____

   A. $\frac{35}{56}$ B. $\frac{91}{117}$ C. $\frac{65}{117}$ D. $\frac{72}{108}$

24) Which of the following fractions equal to $\frac{3}{8}$? _____

   A. $\frac{12}{36}$ B. $\frac{28}{63}$ C. $\frac{42}{112}$ D. $\frac{51}{119}$

Adding and Subtracting Fractions

✎ *Find the sum.*

1) $\frac{4}{7} + \frac{5}{7} =$

2) $\frac{2}{5} + \frac{3}{4} =$

3) $\frac{1}{6} + \frac{5}{6} =$

4) $\frac{7}{9} + \frac{3}{5} =$

5) $\frac{2}{3} + \frac{1}{4} =$

6) $\frac{6}{7} + \frac{4}{9} =$

7) $\frac{7}{8} + \frac{2}{7} =$

8) $\frac{1}{3} + \frac{1}{6} =$

9) $\frac{3}{4} + \frac{5}{9} =$

10) $\frac{8}{13} + \frac{7}{8} =$

11) $\frac{4}{15} + \frac{2}{3} =$

12) $\frac{8}{9} + \frac{1}{3} =$

✎ *Find the difference.*

13) $\frac{7}{9} - \frac{2}{9} =$

14) $\frac{5}{8} - \frac{1}{2} =$

15) $\frac{7}{8} - \frac{1}{4} =$

16) $\frac{2}{3} - \frac{1}{5} =$

17) $\frac{7}{9} - \frac{3}{10} =$

18) $\frac{2}{3} - \frac{1}{4} =$

19) $\frac{5}{6} - \frac{2}{9} =$

20) $\frac{1}{2} - \frac{3}{8} =$

21) $\frac{7}{9} - \frac{3}{11} =$

22) $\frac{12}{13} - \frac{6}{15} =$

23) $\frac{4}{9} - \frac{1}{10} =$

24) $\frac{6}{7} - \frac{5}{9} =$

25) $\frac{14}{15} - \frac{1}{2} =$

26) $\frac{4}{5} - \frac{2}{7} =$

27) $\frac{6}{7} - \frac{3}{8} =$

28) $\frac{3}{5} - \frac{3}{8} =$

29) $\frac{4}{9} - \frac{1}{7} =$

30) $\frac{6}{10} - \frac{2}{9} =$

Multiplying and Dividing Fractions

✎ *Find the value of each expression in lowest terms.*

1) $\frac{2}{5} \times \frac{1}{2} =$

2) $\frac{5}{6} \times \frac{2}{3} =$

3) $\frac{2}{7} \times \frac{5}{6} =$

4) $\frac{1}{2} \times \frac{5}{9} =$

5) $\frac{3}{10} \times \frac{5}{3} =$

6) $\frac{8}{7} \times \frac{14}{32} =$

7) $\frac{6}{7} \times \frac{1}{12} =$

8) $\frac{4}{9} \times \frac{3}{8} =$

9) $\frac{7}{8} \times \frac{12}{14} =$

10) $\frac{9}{10} \times \frac{5}{9} =$

11) $\frac{1}{2} \times \frac{2}{3} =$

12) $\frac{7}{15} \times \frac{5}{7} =$

✎ *Find the value of each expression in lowest terms.*

13) $\frac{2}{5} \div \frac{1}{2} =$

14) $\frac{1}{2} \div \frac{1}{5} =$

15) $\frac{3}{7} \div \frac{5}{7} =$

16) $\frac{4}{9} \div \frac{5}{6} =$

17) $\frac{3}{7} \div \frac{6}{14} =$

18) $\frac{4}{5} \div \frac{2}{10} =$

19) $\frac{6}{7} \div \frac{3}{2} =$

20) $\frac{7}{12} \div \frac{5}{6} =$

21) $\frac{3}{5} \div \frac{6}{5} =$

22) $\frac{7}{10} \div \frac{15}{3} =$

23) $\frac{12}{20} \div \frac{6}{15} =$

24) $\frac{3}{14} \div \frac{12}{9} =$

25) $\frac{6}{9} \div \frac{6}{7} =$

26) $\frac{9}{15} \div \frac{6}{10} =$

27) $\frac{1}{2} \div \frac{8}{10} =$

28) $\frac{5}{7} \div \frac{3}{4} =$

29) $\frac{5}{9} \div \frac{7}{3} =$

30) $\frac{2}{5} \div \frac{5}{2} =$

Adding and Subtracting Mixed Numbers

✍ **Find the sum.**

1) $3\frac{1}{3} + 2\frac{1}{4} =$

2) $5\frac{2}{3} + 1\frac{1}{6} =$

3) $8\frac{2}{5} + 1\frac{1}{2} =$

4) $2\frac{2}{3} + 2\frac{1}{6} =$

5) $3\frac{5}{9} + 1\frac{1}{3} =$

6) $2\frac{6}{7} + 1\frac{1}{2} =$

7) $6\frac{1}{10} + 2\frac{1}{5} =$

8) $4\frac{3}{7} + 2\frac{3}{5} =$

9) $1\frac{1}{4} + 2\frac{4}{5} =$

10) $2\frac{2}{5} + 5\frac{1}{3} =$

✍ **Find the difference.**

11) $5\frac{1}{5} - 2\frac{3}{4} =$

12) $3\frac{3}{5} - 1\frac{5}{6} =$

13) $2\frac{8}{10} - 1\frac{1}{3} =$

14) $7\frac{1}{2} - 3\frac{1}{5} =$

15) $4\frac{5}{6} - 1\frac{3}{12} =$

16) $4\frac{5}{7} - 3\frac{5}{14} =$

17) $5\frac{3}{8} - 5\frac{2}{12} =$

18) $7\frac{8}{11} - 2\frac{7}{22} =$

19) $10\frac{4}{7} - 10\frac{1}{3} =$

20) $9\frac{4}{7} - 7\frac{6}{7} =$

21) $6\frac{6}{9} - 2\frac{1}{3} =$

22) $1\frac{1}{2} - 1\frac{1}{5} =$

23) $14\frac{5}{6} - 10\frac{1}{3} =$

24) $7\frac{3}{5} - 4\frac{1}{2} =$

25) $3\frac{5}{6} - 3\frac{2}{3} =$

26) $11\frac{8}{9} - 14\frac{2}{3} =$

Multiplying and Dividing Mixed Numbers

✎ *Find the product.*

1) $2\frac{2}{5} \times 4\frac{1}{10} =$

6) $5\frac{1}{2} \times 3\frac{5}{6} =$

2) $6\frac{1}{6} \times 1\frac{1}{6} =$

7) $4\frac{5}{6} \times 1\frac{2}{3} =$

3) $3\frac{3}{4} \times 4\frac{1}{5} =$

8) $7\frac{1}{8} \times 2\frac{1}{4} =$

4) $2\frac{1}{3} \times 3\frac{3}{5} =$

9) $3\frac{2}{3} \times 4\frac{1}{6} =$

5) $4\frac{2}{3} \times 1\frac{5}{6} =$

10) $4\frac{4}{9} \times 2\frac{1}{18} =$

✎ *Find the quotient.*

11) $4\frac{1}{2} \div 2\frac{1}{6} =$

19) $6\frac{7}{8} \div 3\frac{1}{4} =$

12) $5\frac{3}{5} \div 3\frac{2}{3} =$

20) $5\frac{9}{14} \div 4\frac{1}{7} =$

13) $8\frac{5}{6} \div 2\frac{1}{3} =$

21) $3\frac{5}{7} \div 2\frac{7}{9} =$

14) $7\frac{5}{7} \div 5\frac{4}{7} =$

22) $3\frac{1}{3} \div 2\frac{1}{2} =$

15) $7\frac{5}{9} \div 6\frac{1}{3} =$

23) $4\frac{5}{8} \div 2\frac{1}{4} =$

16) $9\frac{5}{9} \div 4\frac{1}{3} =$

24) $3\frac{3}{5} \div \frac{1}{10} =$

17) $7\frac{4}{7} \div 6\frac{1}{2} =$

25) $7\frac{2}{9} \div 3\frac{2}{3} =$

18) $5\frac{6}{7} \div 3\frac{1}{2} =$

26) $4\frac{4}{5} \div 2\frac{1}{6} =$

Adding and Subtracting Decimals

✍ **Add and subtract decimals.**

1)
$$\begin{array}{r} 45.12 \\ -\ 25.31 \\ \hline \end{array}$$

4)
$$\begin{array}{r} 17.33 \\ -\ 11.28 \\ \hline \end{array}$$

7)
$$\begin{array}{r} 95.65 \\ -\ 89.23 \\ \hline \end{array}$$

2)
$$\begin{array}{r} 33.72 \\ +\ 21.21 \\ \hline \end{array}$$

5)
$$\begin{array}{r} 85.69 \\ +\ 73.28 \\ \hline \end{array}$$

8)
$$\begin{array}{r} 57.55 \\ +\ 31.85 \\ \hline \end{array}$$

3)
$$\begin{array}{r} 52.34 \\ +\ 43.62 \\ \hline \end{array}$$

6)
$$\begin{array}{r} 46.52 \\ -\ 33.78 \\ \hline \end{array}$$

9)
$$\begin{array}{r} 36.75 \\ -\ 29.30 \\ \hline \end{array}$$

✍ **Find the missing number.**

10) ___ $+ 8.5 = 12.35$

11) $5.45 +$ ___ $= 8.25$

12) $9.74 +$ ___ $= 13.2$

13) $7.28 -$ ___ $= 3.56$

14) ___ $- 72.35 = 12.14$

15) ___ $- 23.56 = 2.75$

16) $14.98 +$ ___ $= 21.08$

17) ___ $- 25.35 = 17.88$

18) ___ $+ 31.22 = 68.76$

19) $36.50 +$ ___ $= 90.88$

Multiplying and Dividing Decimals

✏️ *Find the product.*

1) $1.8 \times 2.4 =$

2) $7.5 \times 0.9 =$

3) $4.25 \times 1.2 =$

4) $1.25 \times 0.8 =$

5) $3.50 \times 2.5 =$

6) $0.85 \times 0.9 =$

7) $0.75 \times 0.25 =$

8) $14.21 \times 1.52 =$

9) $21.23 \times 3.45 =$

10) $8.74 \times 2.91 =$

11) $12.95 \times 10.25 =$

12) $14.39 \times 7.46 =$

✏️ *Find the quotient.*

13) $2.54 \div 50 =$

14) $3.75 \div 100 =$

15) $7.25 \div 5 =$

16) $12.5 \div 1,000 =$

17) $14.75 \div 0.8 =$

18) $21.85 \div 25 =$

19) $0.25 \div 1,000 =$

20) $42.5 \div 2.5 =$

21) $35.9 \div 0.8 =$

22) $11.6 \div 4 =$

23) $55.5 \div 7.5 =$

24) $14.45 \div 0.5 =$

Comparing Decimals

✎ *Write the correct comparison symbol (>, < or =).*

1) 0.72 ☐ 0.722

2) 0.035 ☐ 0.0035

3) 2.702 ☐ 2.072

4) 1.84 ☐ 1.48

5) 6.045 ☐ 6.405

6) 7.21 ☐ 7.12

7) 15.85 ☐ 15.085

8) 17.12 ☐ 71.21

9) 3.095 ☐ 3.10

10) 0.825 ☐ 8.25

11) 9.75 ☐ 0.975

12) 5.48 ☐ 5.084

13) 4.98 ☐ 4.94

14) 72.075 ☐ 72.057

15) 33.046 ☐ 33.12

16) 14.321 ☐ 14.321

17) 8.73 ☐ 87.3

18) 45.60 ☐ 45.06

19) 3.925 ☐ 3.0925

20) 75.20 ☐ 72.50

Rounding Decimals

✎ *Round each decimal to the nearest whole number.*

1) 45.65   3) 82.21   5) 5.65

2) 0.49   4) 32.12   6) 11.09

✎ *Round each decimal to the nearest tenth.*

7) 12.562   9) 42.086   11) 12.46

8) 14.256   10) 13.737   12) 9.196

✎ *Round each decimal to the nearest hundredth.*

13) 1.826   15) 21.089   17) 17.498

14) 9.468   16) 10.062   18) 37.831

✎ *Round each decimal to the nearest thousandth.*

19) 1.2867   21) 12.7953   23) 28.1897

20) 3.7643   22) 0.7954   24) 16.7988

Factoring Numbers

✍ *List all positive factors of each number.*

1) 65

2) 10

3) 14

4) 46

5) 74

6) 92

7) 43

8) 30

9) 38

10) 41

11) 58

12) 29

13) 69

14) 76

15) 37

16) 50

17) 21

18) 100

19) 78

20) 86

21) 57

22) 76

23) 44

24) 90

Greatest Common Factor

✎ *Find the GCF for each number pair.*

1) 12, 18

2) 20, 8

3) 14, 30

4) 8, 12

5) 20, 50

6) 68, 80

7) 64, 30

8) 26, 85

9) 6, 36

10) 15, 50

11) 18, 60

12) 16, 46

13) 28, 70

14) 36, 78

15) 10, 32

16) 22, 48

17) 24, 52

18) 46, 20

19) 78, 40

20) 21, 84

21) 35, 60

22) 52, 90

23) 39, 72

24) 35, 75

Least Common Multiple

✎ *Find the LCM for each number pair.*

1) 10, 12

2) 16, 24

3) 8, 20

4) 8, 14

5) 15, 20

6) 48, 30

7) 15, 10

8) 12, 33

9) 15, 30

10) 18, 24

11) 27, 36

12) 63, 18

13) 44, 20

14) 16, 24

15) 4, 13

16) 19, 57

17) 34, 10

18) 72, 12

19) 30, 50

20) 17, 85

21) 40, 25

22) 70, 35

23) 80, 30

24) 20, 26

Answers

Simplifying Fractions

1) $\frac{5}{9}$

2) $\frac{3}{7}$

3) $\frac{1}{12}$

4) $\frac{1}{2}$

5) $\frac{2}{5}$

6) $\frac{1}{3}$

7) $\frac{2}{5}$

8) $\frac{1}{6}$

9) $\frac{1}{6}$

10) $\frac{5}{9}$

11) $\frac{2}{3}$

12) $\frac{3}{8}$

13) $\frac{4}{13}$

14) $\frac{2}{5}$

15) $\frac{9}{20}$

16) $\frac{5}{14}$

17) $\frac{4}{7}$

18) $\frac{1}{6}$

19) $\frac{2}{3}$

20) $\frac{1}{2}$

21) $\frac{2}{5}$

22) D

23) B

24) C

Adding and Subtracting Fractions

1) $\frac{9}{7}$

2) $\frac{23}{20}$

3) 1

4) $\frac{62}{45}$

5) $\frac{11}{12}$

6) $\frac{82}{63}$

7) $\frac{65}{56}$

8) $\frac{1}{2}$

9) $\frac{47}{36}$

10) $\frac{155}{104}$

11) $\frac{14}{15}$

12) $\frac{11}{9}$

13) $\frac{5}{9}$

14) $\frac{1}{8}$

15) $\frac{5}{8}$

16) $\frac{7}{15}$

17) $\frac{49}{90}$

18) $\frac{5}{12}$

19) $\frac{11}{18}$

20) $\frac{1}{8}$

21) $\frac{56}{99}$

22) $\frac{34}{65}$

23) $\frac{31}{90}$

24) $\frac{19}{63}$

25) $\frac{13}{30}$

26) $\frac{18}{35}$

27) $\frac{27}{56}$

28) $\frac{9}{40}$

29) $\frac{19}{63}$

30) $\frac{17}{45}$

Multiplying and Dividing Fractions

1) $\frac{1}{5}$

2) $\frac{5}{9}$

3) $\frac{5}{21}$

4) $\frac{5}{18}$

5) $\frac{1}{2}$

6) $\frac{1}{2}$

7) $\frac{1}{14}$

8) $\frac{1}{6}$

9) $\frac{3}{4}$

10) $\frac{1}{2}$

11) $\frac{1}{3}$

12) $\frac{1}{3}$

13) $\frac{4}{5}$

14) $\frac{5}{2}$

15) $\frac{3}{5}$

16) $\frac{8}{15}$

17) 1

18) 4

19) $\frac{4}{7}$

20) $\frac{7}{10}$

21) $\frac{1}{2}$

22) $\frac{7}{50}$

23) $\frac{3}{2}$

24) $\frac{9}{56}$

25) $\frac{7}{9}$

26) 1

27) $\frac{5}{8}$

28) $\frac{20}{21}$

29) $\frac{5}{21}$

30) $\frac{4}{25}$

Adding and Subtracting Mixed Numbers

1) $5\frac{7}{12}$

2) $6\frac{5}{6}$

3) $9\frac{9}{10}$

4) $4\frac{5}{6}$

5) $4\frac{8}{9}$

6) $4\frac{5}{14}$

7) $8\frac{3}{10}$

8) $7\frac{1}{35}$

9) $4\frac{1}{20}$

10) $7\frac{11}{15}$

11) $2\frac{9}{20}$

12) $1\frac{23}{30}$

13) $1\frac{7}{15}$

14) $4\frac{3}{10}$

15) $3\frac{7}{12}$

16) $1\frac{5}{14}$

17) $\frac{5}{24}$

18) $5\frac{9}{22}$

19) $\frac{5}{21}$

20) $1\frac{5}{7}$

21) $4\frac{1}{3}$

22) $\frac{3}{10}$

23) $4\frac{1}{2}$

24) $3\frac{1}{10}$

25) $\frac{1}{6}$

26) $-2\frac{7}{9}$

Multiplying and Dividing Mixed Numbers

1) $9\frac{21}{25}$

2) $7\frac{7}{36}$

3) $15\frac{3}{4}$

4) $8\frac{2}{5}$

5) $8\frac{5}{9}$

6) $21\frac{1}{12}$

7) $8\frac{1}{18}$

8) $16\frac{1}{32}$

9) $15\frac{5}{8}$

10) $9\frac{11}{81}$

11) $2\frac{1}{13}$

12) $1\frac{29}{55}$

13) $3\frac{11}{14}$

14) $1\frac{5}{13}$

15) $1\frac{11}{57}$

16) $2\frac{8}{39}$

17) $1\frac{15}{91}$

18) $1\frac{33}{49}$

19) $2\frac{3}{26}$

20) $1\frac{21}{58}$

21) $1\frac{59}{175}$

22) $1\frac{1}{3}$

23) $2\frac{1}{18}$

24) 36

25) $1\frac{32}{33}$

26) $2\frac{14}{65}$

Adding and Subtracting Decimals

1) 19.81
2) 54.93
3) 95.96
4) 6.05
5) 158.97
6) 12.74
7) 6.42

8) 89.4
9) 7.45
10) 3.85
11) 2.8
12) 3.46
13) 3.72
14) 84.49

15) 26.31
16) 6.1
17) 43.23
18) 37.54
19) 54.38

Multiplying and Dividing Decimals

1) 4.32
2) 6.75
3) 5.1
4) 1
5) 8.75
6) 0.765
7) 0.1875
8) 21.5992
9) 73.2435

10) 25.4334
11) 132.7375
12) 107.3494
13) 0.0508
14) 0.0375
15) 1.45
16) 0.0125
17) 18.4375
18) 0.874

19) 0.00025
20) 17
21) 44.875
22) 2.9
23) 7.4
24) 28.9

Comparing Decimals

1) <
2) >
3) >
4) >
5) <
6) >
7) >

8) <
9) <
10) <
11) >
12) >
13) >
14) >

15) <
16) =
17) <
18) >
19) >
20) >

Rounding Decimals

1) 46
2) 0
3) 82
4) 32
5) 6
6) 11
7) 12.6
8) 14.3

9) 42.1
10) 13.7
11) 12.5
12) 9.2
13) 1.83
14) 9.47
15) 21.09
16) 10.06

17) 17.50
18) 37.83
19) 1.287
20) 3.764
21) 12.795
22) 0.795
23) 28.190
24) 16.799

Factoring Numbers

1) 1, 5, 13, 65
2) 1, 2, 5, 10
3) 1, 2, 7, 14
4) 1, 2, 23, 46
5) 1, 2, 37, 74
6) 1, 2, 4, 23, 46, 92
7) 1, 43
8) 1, 2, 3, 5, 6, 10, 15, 30
9) 1, 2, 19, 38
10) 1, 41
11) 1, 2, 29, 58
12) 1, 29

13) 1, 3, 23, 69
14) 1, 2, 4, 19, 38, 76
15) 1, 37
16) 1, 2, 5, 10, 25, 50
17) 1, 3, 7, 21
18) 1, 2, 4, 5, 10, 20, 25, 50, 100
19) 1, 2, 3, 6, 13, 26, 39, 78
20) 1, 2, 43, 86
21) 1, 3, 19, 57
22) 1, 2, 4, 19, 38, 76
23) 1, 2, 4, 11, 22, 44
24) 1, 2, 3, 5, 6, 9, 10, 15, 18, 30, 45, 90

Greatest Common Factor

1) 6
2) 4
3) 2
4) 4
5) 10
6) 4
7) 2
8) 1

9) 6
10) 5
11) 6
12) 2
13) 14
14) 6
15) 2
16) 2

17) 4
18) 2
19) 2
20) 21
21) 5
22) 2
23) 3
24) 5

Least Common Multiple

1) 60
2) 48
3) 40
4) 56
5) 60
6) 240
7) 30
8) 132

9) 30
10) 72
11) 108
12) 126
13) 220
14) 48
15) 52
16) 57

17) 170
18) 72
19) 150
20) 85
21) 200
22) 70
23) 240
24) 260

Chapter 3:

Real Numbers and Integers

Topics that you'll practice in this chapter:

✓ Adding and Subtracting Integers

✓ Multiplying and Dividing Integers

✓ Order of Operations

✓ Ordering Integers and Numbers

✓ Integers and Absolute Value

Adding and Subtracting Integers

✍ *Find each sum.*

1) $71 + (-32) =$

2) $(-23) + (-12) =$

3) $17 + (-36) =$

4) $42 + (-64) =$

5) $(-19) + (-21) + 8 =$

6) $33 + (-17) + 2 =$

7) $18 + (-45) + (-11) + 36 =$

8) $(-23) + (-29) + 12 + 20 =$

9) $24 + (-33) + (40 - 52) =$

10) $31 + (-18) + (13 - 26) =$

✍ *Find each difference.*

11) $(-31) - (-15) =$

12) $27 - (-11) =$

13) $(-52) - 14 =$

14) $36 - (-8) =$

15) $42 - (21 - 59) =$

16) $47 - (-24) - (-12) =$

17) $(12 - 15) - (-24) =$

18) $46 - 19 - (-14) =$

19) $72 - (16 + 8) - (-26) =$

20) $38 - (-19) - (-13) =$

21) $46 - (-29) - (-11) =$

22) $(56 - 41) - (-13) =$

23) $17 - 73 - (-55) =$

24) $77 - (45 + 15) - (-17) =$

25) $64 - (-21) + (-49) =$

26) $76 - (-55) + (-120) =$

Multiplying and Dividing Integers

✎ *Find each product.*

1) $(-11) \times (-9) =$

2) $(-13) \times 6 =$

3) $8 \times (-16) =$

4) $(-3) \times (-17) =$

5) $-(2 - 4) \times (-6) \times 4 =$

6) $(18 - 7) \times (-7) =$

7) $21 \times (-15) \times (-6) =$

8) $(32 - 22) \times (-13) =$

9) $10 \times (-12 + 21) \times 7 =$

10) $(-4) \times (-18) \times (-28) =$

✎ *Find each quotient.*

11) $(-27) \div (-3) =$

12) $(-65) \div (-13) =$

13) $(-72) \div (12) =$

14) $81 \div (-27) =$

15) $(-110) \div 11 =$

16) $(-108) \div (-12) =$

17) $420 \div (-15) =$

18) $(-144) \div (-48) =$

19) $304 \div (-19) =$

20) $-(600) \div (75) =$

21) $(-132) \div (-11) =$

22) $-104 \div (-4) =$

23) $(-342) \div (18) =$

24) $(-294) \div (-14) =$

25) $-(440) \div (-22) =$

26) $(96) \div (-16) =$

Order of Operations

✎ *Evaluate each expression.*

1) $14 + (3 \times 5) =$

2) $45 - (8 \times 4) =$

3) $(11 \times 3) - 25 =$

4) $(18 - 14) - (5 \times 4) =$

5) $65 - (32 \div 4) =$

6) $(15 \times 3) \div (-9) =$

7) $(96 \div 12) \times (-8) =$

8) $(6 \times 4) - (33 - 17) =$

9) $81 - (9 \times 12) + 4 =$

10) $(15 \times (-4)) \div (12 + 3) =$

11) $(-16) + (18 \times 3) - 42 =$

12) $(14 \times 6) - (150 \div 25) =$

13) $(7 \times 12 \div 6) - (19 - 11) =$

14) $(21 + 3 - 18) \times 7 - 4 =$

15) $(41 - 23 + 11) \times (40 \div 8) =$

16) $13 + \left(41 - (36 \div 9) \right) =$

17) $(19 + 8 - 16) + (24 \div 3) =$

18) $(49 - 38) + (17 - 43 - 2) =$

19) $(14 \times 6) + (12 \times 2) - 25 =$

20) $8 + 16 - (9 \times 4) - 88 =$

Ordering Integers and Numbers

✍ **Order each set of integers from least to greatest.**

1) $-9, 12, -4, -1, 13, 20$ ___, ___, ___, ___, ___, ___

2) $15, -20, 14, -16, 2, -4$ ___, ___, ___, ___, ___, ___

3) $-5, 4, -19, 11, -4, -23, 5$ ___, ___, ___, ___, ___, ___

4) $-45, 2, 17, -52, -1, -29$ ___, ___, ___, ___, ___, ___

5) $53, -19, 11, 3, -18, -32$ ___, ___, ___, ___, ___, ___

6) $33, -45, -20, 20, 15, -42, 32, -44$ ___, ___, ___, ___, ___, ___

✍ **Order each set of integers from greatest to least.**

7) $-34, 12, -51, 1, -44, 29, 45$ ___, ___, ___, ___, ___, ___

8) $9, -8, 12, -13, -56, 25, 44$ ___, ___, ___, ___, ___, ___

9) $-97, 14, -21, 53, -45, 22, 14$ ___, ___, ___, ___, ___, ___

10) $-72, 44, 21, -5, -14, 10, 16$ ___, ___, ___, ___, ___, ___

11) $12, -23, -11, 21, 14, 19, -20$ ___, ___, ___, ___, ___, ___

12) $-8, 22, 19, 21, -42, -22, -36$ ___, ___, ___, ___, ___, ___

Integers and Absolute Value

✍ ***Write absolute value of each number.***

1) $|-85| =$

2) $|-66| =$

3) $|-17| =$

4) $|15| =$

5) $|64| =$

6) $|-69| =$

7) $|72| =$

8) $|3| =$

9) $|-41| =$

10) $|-29| =$

11) $|-54|$

12) $|20| =$

13) $|-18| =$

14) $|-44| =$

15) $|-28| =$

16) $|-78| =$

17) $|-70| =$

18) $|-26| =$

19) $|52| =$

20) $|-99| =$

✍ ***Evaluate the value.***

21) $|-10| - \frac{|-15|}{3} =$

22) $12 - |9 - 13| - |-6| =$

23) $\frac{|-55|}{5} \times |-3| =$

24) $\frac{|12 \times -5|}{15} \times \frac{|-32|}{8} =$

25) $|4 \times -6| + \frac{|-85|}{17} =$

26) $\frac{|-33|}{11} \times \frac{|-42|}{7} =$

27) $|-35 + 9| \times \frac{|-7 \times 6|}{3} =$

28) $\frac{|-12 \times 4|}{24} \times |-9| =$

Answers

Adding and Subtracting Integers

1) 39
2) −35
3) −19
4) −22
5) −32
6) 18
7) −2
8) −20
9) −21
10) 0
11) −16
12) 38
13) −66
14) 44
15) 80
16) 83
17) 21
18) 41
19) 74
20) 70
21) 86
22) 28
23) −1
24) 34
25) 36
26) 11

Multiplying and Dividing Integers

1) 99
2) −78
3) −128
4) 51
5) −48
6) −77
7) 1890
8) −130
9) 630
10) −2016
11) 9
12) 5
13) −6
14) −3
15) −10
16) 9
17) −28
18) 3
19) −16
20) −8
21) 12
22) 26
23) −19
24) 21
25) 20
26) −6

Order of Operations

1) 29
2) 13
3) 8
4) −16
5) 57
6) −5
7) −64
8) 8
9) −23
10) −4
11) −4
12) 78
13) 6
14) 38
15) 145
16) 50
17) 19
18) −18
19) 83
20) −100

Ordering Integers and Numbers

1) −9, −4, −1, 12, 13, 20
2) −20, −16, −4, 2, 14, 15
3) −23, −19, −5, −4, 4, 5, 11
4) −52, −45, −29, −1, 2, 17
5) −32, −19, −18, 3, 11, 53
6) −45, −44, −42, −20, 15, 20, 32, 33

7) $45, 29, 12, 1, -34, -44, -51$
8) $44, 25, 12, 9, -8, -13, -56$
9) $53, 22, 14, 14, -21, -45, -97$

10) $44, 21, 16, 10, -5, -14, -72$
11) $21, 19, 14, 12, -11, -20, -23$
12) $22, 21, 19, -8, -22, -36, -42$

Integers and Absolute Value

1) 85
2) 66
3) 17
4) 15
5) 64
6) 69
7) 72
8) 3
9) 41
10) 29

11) 54
12) 20
13) 18
14) 44
15) 28
16) 78
17) 70
18) 26
19) 52
20) 99

21) 5
22) 2
23) 33
24) 16
25) 29
26) 18
27) 364
28) 18

Chapter 4:

Proportions, Ratios, and Percent

Topics that you'll practice in this chapter:

- ✓ Simplifying Ratios
- ✓ Proportional Ratios
- ✓ Similarity and Ratios
- ✓ Ratio and Rates Word Problems
- ✓ Percentage Calculations
- ✓ Percent Problems
- ✓ Discount, Tax and Tip
- ✓ Percent of Change
- ✓ Simple Interest

Simplifying Ratios

✎ *Reduce each ratio.*

1) $45:15 = $ ___ : ___

2) $40:54 = $ ___ : ___

3) $8:12 = $ ___ : ___

4) $18:30 = $ ___ : ___

5) $24:40 = $ ___ : ___

6) $65:85 = $ ___ : ___

7) $36:48 = $ ___ : ___

8) $72:90 = $ ___ : ___

9) $64:40 = $ ___ : ___

10) $14:24 = $ ___ : ___

11) $20:70 = $ ___ : ___

12) $144:72 = $ ___ : ___

13) $56:80 = $ ___ : ___

14) $39:117 = $ ___ : ___

15) $16:40 = $ ___ : ___

16) $64:38 = $ ___ : ___

17) $84:32 = $ ___ : ___

18) $96:108 = $ ___ : ___

19) $33:66 = $ ___ : ___

20) $42:24 = $ ___ : ___

21) $58:74 = $ ___ : ___

22) $21:63 = $ ___ : ___

23) $90:44 = $ ___ : ___

24) $25:65 = $ ___ : ___

✎ *Write each ratio as a fraction in simplest form.*

25) $4:12 = $

26) $16:20 = $

27) $46:50 = $

28) $32:48 = $

29) $7:14 = $

30) $25:45 = $

31) $34:80 = $

32) $24:36 = $

33) $6:18 = $

34) $38:94 = $

35) $22:30 = $

36) $76:54 = $

37) $26:117 = $

38) $15:35 = $

39) $15:25 = $

40) $52:60 = $

41) $58:66 = $

42) $21:84 = $

43) $33:121 = $

44) $27:99 = $

45) $40:60 = $

Proportional Ratios

✎ **Fill in the blanks; solve each proportion.**

1) $2 : 9 \quad = \quad \underline{} : 54$

2) $3 : 7 \quad = \quad 21 : \underline{}$

3) $1 : 2 \quad = \quad \underline{} : 70$

4) $4 : 5 \quad = \quad 20 : \underline{}$

5) $3 : 8 \quad = \quad 48 : \underline{}$

6) $2 : 7 \quad = \quad \underline{} : 28$

7) $5 : 2 \quad = \quad \underline{} : 24$

8) $4 : 3 \quad = \quad \underline{} : 36$

9) $4 : 9 \quad = \quad \underline{} : 81$

10) $3 : 5 \quad = \quad \underline{} : 40$

11) $6 : 7 \quad = \quad 30 : \underline{}$

12) $7 : 5 \quad = \quad 49 : \underline{}$

✎ **State if each pair of ratios form a proportion.**

13) $\frac{5}{6}$ and $\frac{25}{30}$

14) $\frac{4}{3}$ and $\frac{28}{20}$

15) $\frac{15}{9}$ and $\frac{45}{27}$

16) $\frac{9}{5}$ and $\frac{117}{65}$

17) $\frac{2}{7}$ and $\frac{14}{42}$

18) $\frac{7}{3}$ and $\frac{77}{33}$

19) $\frac{15}{18}$ and $\frac{45}{54}$

20) $\frac{7}{15}$ and $\frac{28}{75}$

21) $\frac{3}{20}$ and $\frac{9}{60}$

22) $\frac{21}{25}$ and $\frac{105}{125}$

23) $\frac{16}{21}$ and $\frac{96}{126}$

24) $\frac{6}{13}$ and $\frac{42}{91}$

✎ **Solve each proportion.**

25) $\frac{3}{10} = \frac{6}{x}, x = \underline{}$

26) $\frac{4}{9} = \frac{16}{x}, x = \underline{}$

27) $\frac{9}{2} = \frac{153}{x}, x = \underline{}$

28) $\frac{12}{17} = \frac{x}{102}, x = \underline{}$

29) $\frac{2}{5} = \frac{x}{45}, x = \underline{}$

30) $\frac{4}{13} = \frac{24}{x}, x = \underline{}$

31) $\frac{5}{6} = \frac{100}{x}, x = \underline{}$

32) $\frac{3}{16} = \frac{12}{x}, x = \underline{}$

33) $\frac{4}{9} = \frac{x}{54}, x = \underline{}$

34) $\frac{2}{7} = \frac{x}{112}, x = \underline{}$

35) $\frac{6}{19} = \frac{x}{76}, x = \underline{}$

36) $\frac{7}{20} = \frac{x}{200}, x = \underline{}$

Similarity and Ratios

🖎 *Each pair of figures is similar. Find the missing side.*

1)

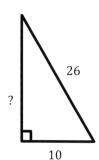

2)

3)

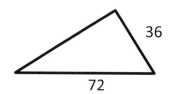

4)

🖎 *Solve.*

5) Two rectangles are similar. The first is 12 feet wide and 36 feet long. The second is 16 feet wide. What is the length of the second rectangle? _____

6) Two rectangles are similar. One is 4.5 meters by 15 meters. The longer side of the second rectangle is 25 meters. What is the other side of the second rectangle? _____

7) A building casts a shadow 18 ft long. At the same time a girl 4.5 ft tall casts a shadow 1.5 ft long. How tall is the building? _____

8) The scale of a map of Texas is 3 inches: 50 miles. If you measure the distance from Dallas to Martin County as 15 inches, approximately how far is Martin County from Dallas? _____

Ratio and Rates Word Problems

✍ *Solve each word problem.*

1) Bob has 21 red cards and 30 green cards. What is the ratio of Bob's red cards to his green cards? _____

2) In a party, 12 soft drinks are required for every 15 guests. If there are 270 guests, how many soft drinks is required? _____

3) In Jack's class, 16 of the students are tall and 12 are short. In Michael's class 48 students are tall and 36 students are short. Which class has a higher ratio of tall to short students? _____

4) The price of 4 apples at the Quick Market is $1.54. The price of 6 of the same apples at Walmart is $2.24. Which place is the better buy? _____

5) The bakers at a Bakery can make 200 bagels in 5 hours. How many bagels can they bake in 12 hours? What is that rate per hour? _____

6) You can buy 7 cans of green beans at a supermarket for $3.50. How much does it cost to buy 20 cans of green beans? _____

7) The ratio of boys to girls in a class is 5:7. If there are 25 boys in the class, how many girls are in that class? _____

8) The ratio of red marbles to blue marbles in a bag is 5:9. If there are 70 marbles in the bag, how many of the marbles are red? _____

Percentage Calculations

✎ **Calculate the given percent of each value.**

1) 15% of 30 = ____   7) 75% of 80 = ____   13) 80% of 180 = ____

2) 16% of 40 = ____   8) 45% of 120 = ____   14) 27% of 700 = ____

3) 25% of 80 = ____   9) 12% of 500 = ____   15) 48% of 400 = ____

4) 35% of 60 = ____   10) 14% of 150 = ____   16) 85% of 300 = ____

5) 24% of 50 = ____   11) 45% of 200 = ____   17) 44% of 200 = ____

6) 18% of 150 = ____   12) 65% of 140 = ____   18) 57% of 600 = ____

✎ **Calculate the percent of each given value.**

19) ____% of 50 = 17.5   24) ____% of 80 = 36

20) ____% of 300 = 66   25) ____% of 250 = 45

21) ____% of 160 = 88   26) ____% of 70 = 3.5

22) ____% of 30 = 6   27) ____% of 400 = 48

23) ____% of 60 = 9   28) ___% of 160 = 120

✎ **Solve each percent problem.**

29) A Cinema has 300 seats. 252 seats were sold for the current movie. What percent of seats are empty? _____ %

30) There are 24 boys and 36 girls in a class. 70% of the students in the class take the bus to school. How many students do not take the bus to school? _____

Percent Problems

✍ **Solve each problem.**

1) 15 is what percent of 40? ____%

2) 24 is what percent of 96? ____%

3) 6 is what percent of 30? ____%

4) 45 is what percent of 120? ____%

5) 36 is what percent of 50? ____%

6) 42 is what percent of 70? ____%

7) 80 is what percent of 200? ____%

8) 30 is what percent of 75? ____%

9) 64 is what percent of 800? ____%

10) 50 *is what percent of* 125? ___%

11) 49 *is what percent of* 350? ___%

12) 48 *is what percent of* 240? ___%

13) 75 *is what percent of* 600? ___%

14) 32 *is what percent of* 160? ___%

15) 63 *is what percent of* 700? ___%

16) 12 *is what percent of* 300? ___%

17) 85 *is what percent of* 500? ___%

18) 16 *is what percent of* 400? ___%

✍ **Solve each percent word problem.**

19) There are 50 employees in a company. On a certain day, 38 were present. What percent showed up for work? _____%

20) A metal bar weighs 42 ounces. 25% of the bar is gold. How many ounces of gold are in the bar? _____

21) A crew is made up of 30 women; the rest are men. If 15% of the crew are women, how many people are in the crew? _____

22) There are 64 students in a class and 24 of them are girls. What percent are boys? _____%

23) The Royals softball team played 85 games and won 68 of them. What percent of the games did they lose? _____%

Discount, Tax and Tip

✎ *Find the selling price of each item.*

1) Original price of a computer: $550

   Tax: 4%   Selling price: $_____

2) Original price of a laptop: $620

   Tax: 7%   Selling price: $_____

3) Original price of a sofa: $650

   Tax: 8%   Selling price: $_____

4) Original price of a car: $24,000

   Tax: 9%   Selling price: $_____

5) Original price of a Table: $160

   Tax: 4%   Selling price: $_____

6) Original price of a house: $180,000

   Tax: 12%   Selling price: $_____

7) Original price of a tablet: $540

   Discount: 25%   Selling price: $_____

8) Original price of a chair: $125

   Discount: 20%   Selling price: $_____

9) Original price of a book: $18

   Discount: 20%   Selling price: $_____

10) Original price of a cellphone: $480

    Discount: 8%   Selling price: $_____

11) Food bill: $32

    Tip: 15%   Price: $_____

12) Food bill: $45

    Tipp: 10%   Price: $_____

13) Food bill: $42

    Tip: 15%   Price: $_____

14) Food bill: $24

    Tipp: 30%   Price: $_____

✎ *Solve each word problem.*

15) Nicolas hired a moving company. The company charged $500 for its services, and Nicolas gives the movers a 12% tip. How much does Nicolas tip the movers? $_____

16) Mason has lunch at a restaurant and the cost of his meal is $30. Mason wants to leave a 9% tip. What is Mason's total bill including tip? $_____

17) The sales tax in Texas is 7.75% and an item costs $600. How much is the tax? $_____

18) The price of a table at Best Buy is $180. If the sales tax is 5%, what is the final price of the table including tax? $_____

Percent of Change

✍ *Find each percent of change.*

1) From 80 to 400. ___ %

2) From 45 ft to 135 ft. ___ %

3) From $600 to $150. ___ %

4) From 25 cm to 150 cm. ___ %

5) From 350 to 70. ___ %

6) From 72 to 18. ___ %

7) From 160 to 40. ___ %

8) From 125 to 50. ___ %

9) From 60 to 450. ___ %

10) From 45 to 27. ___ %

✍ *Solve each percent of change word problem.*

11) Bob got a raise, and his hourly wage increased from $20 to $24. What is the percent increase? _____ %

12) The price of a pair of shoes increases from $24 to $36. What is the percent increase? ___ %

13) At a coffeeshop, the price of a cup of coffee increased from $1.25 to $1.60. What is the percent increase in the cost of the coffee? _____ %

14) 12 cm are cut from a 30 cm board. What is the percent decrease in length? _____ %

15) In a class, the number of students has been increased from 22 to 33. What is the percent increase? _____ %

16) The price of gasoline rose from $1.5 to $2.4 in one month. By what percent did the gas price rise? _____ %

17) A shirt was originally priced at $55. It went on sale for $50.6. What was the percent that the shirt was discounted? _____ %

Simple Interest

✎ ***Determine the simple interest for these loans.***

1) $720 at 8% for 4 years. $ _____

2) $3,500 at 5% for 6 years. $ _____

3) $3,400 at 6% for 10 years. $ _____

4) $7,000 at 3.5% for 9 months. $ _____

5) $1,000 at 3% for 6 months. $ _____

6) $36,000 at 6.5% for 3 years. $ _____

7) $24,000 at 4.5% for 3 years. $ _____

8) $11,000 at 6.5% for 6 years. $ _____

9) $4,000 at 3.5 % for 6 months. $ _____

10) $52,000 at 6.2% for 7 years. $ _____

✎ ***Solve each simple interest word problem.***

11)   A new car, valued at $35,000, depreciates at 8% per year. What is the value of the car one year after purchase? $_____

12)   Sara puts $6,000 into an investment yielding 4.5% annual simple interest; she left the money in for seven years. How much interest does Sara get at the end of those seven years? $_____

13)   A bank is offering 4.5% simple interest on a savings account. If you deposit $18,500, how much interest will you earn in four years? $_____

14) $500 interest is earned on a principal of $2,500 at a simple interest rate of 4% interest per year. For how many years was the principal invested? _____

15) In how many years will $3,200 yield an interest of $768 at 8% simple interest? _____

16)   Jim invested $6,000 in a bond at a yearly rate of 6.5%. He earned $780 in interest. How long was the money invested? _____

Answers

Simplifying Ratios

1) $3 : 1$
2) $20 : 27$
3) $2 : 3$
4) $3 : 5$
5) $3 : 5$
6) $13 : 17$
7) $3 : 4$
8) $4 : 5$
9) $8 : 5$
10) $7 : 12$
11) $2 : 7$
12) $2 : 1$
13) $7 : 10$
14) $1 : 3$
15) $2 : 5$
16) $32 : 19$
17) $21 : 8$
18) $8 : 9$

19) $1 : 2$
20) $7 : 4$
21) $29 : 37$
22) $1 : 3$
23) $45 : 22$
24) $5 : 13$
25) $\frac{1}{3}$
26) $\frac{4}{5}$
27) $\frac{23}{25}$
28) $\frac{2}{3}$
29) $\frac{1}{2}$
30) $\frac{5}{9}$
31) $\frac{17}{40}$
32) $\frac{2}{3}$

33) $\frac{1}{3}$
34) $\frac{19}{47}$
35) $\frac{11}{15}$
36) $\frac{38}{27}$
37) $\frac{2}{9}$
38) $\frac{3}{7}$
39) $\frac{3}{5}$
40) $\frac{13}{15}$
41) $\frac{29}{33}$
42) $\frac{1}{4}$
43) $\frac{3}{11}$
44) $\frac{3}{11}$
45) $\frac{2}{3}$

Proportional Ratios

1) 12
2) 49
3) 35
4) 25
5) 128
6) 8
7) 60
8) 48
9) 36
10) 24
11) 35
12) 35

13) Yes
14) NO
15) Yes
16) Yes
17) No
18) Yes
19) Yes
20) No
21) Yes
22) Yes
23) Yes
24) Yes

25) 20
26) 36
27) 34
28) 72
29) 18
30) 78
31) 120
32) 64
33) 24
34) 32
35) 24
36) 70

Similarity and ratios

1) 16	4) 27	7) 54 feet
2) 3	5) 48 feet	8) 250 miles
3) 18	6) 7.5 meters	

Ratio and Rates Word Problems

1) 7 : 10	5) 480, the rate is 40 per hour.
2) 216	6) $10
3) The ratio for both classes is 4 to 3.	7) 35
4) Walmart is a better buy.	8) 25

Percentage Calculations

1) 4.5	11) 90	21) 55%
2) 6.4	12) 91	22) 20%
3) 20	13) 144	23) 15%
4) 21	14) 189	24) 45%
5) 12	15) 192	25) 18%
6) 27	16) 255	26) 5%
7) 60	17) 88	27) 12%
8) 54	18) 342	28) 75%
9) 60	19) 35%	29) 16%
10) 21	20) 22%	30) 18

Percent Problems

1) 37.5%	9) 8%	17) 17%
2) 25%	10) 40%	18) 4%
3) 20%	11) 14%	19) 76%
4) 37.5%	12) 20%	20) 10.5 ounces
5) 72%	13) 12.5%	21) 200
6) 60%	14) 20%	22) 62.5%
7) 40%	15) 9%	23) 20%
8) 40%	16) 4%	

Discount, Tax and Tip

1) $572.00	4) $26,160	7) $405.00
2) $663.40	5) $166.40	8) $100.0
3) $702.00	6) $201,600	9) $14.40

10) $441.60
11) $36.80
12) $49.50

13) $48.30
14) $31.20
15) $60.00

16) $32.70
17) $46.50
18) $189.00

Percent of Change

1) 500%
2) 300%
3) 25%
4) 600%
5) 20%
6) 25%

7) 25%
8) 40%
9) 750%
10) 60%
11) 20%
12) 50%

13) 28%
14) 40%
15) 50%
16) 60%
17) 8%

Simple Interest

1) $230.40
2) $1050.00
3) $2040.00
4) $183.75
5) $15.00
6) $7020.00

7) $3240.00
8) $4290.00
9) $70.00
10) $22,568.00
11) $32,200.00
12) $1,890.00

13) $3,330.00
14)   5 years
15)   3 years
16)   2 years

Chapter 5:

Algebraic Expressions

Topics that you'll practice in this chapter:

- ✓ Simplifying Variable Expressions
- ✓ Simplifying Polynomial Expressions
- ✓ Translate Phrases into an Algebraic Statement
- ✓ The Distributive Property
- ✓ Evaluating One Variable Expressions
- ✓ Evaluating Two Variables Expressions
- ✓ Combining like Terms

Simplifying Variable Expressions

✎ **Simplify each expression.**

1) $7(3x + 2) =$

2) $(-4)(3x - 5) =$

3) $4x + 5 - 6x =$

4) $-2x - 5x^2 - x^2 =$

5) $5x + 7x^2 - 6x =$

6) $12x^2 - 4x - 9x^2 =$

7) $11x^2 - 19x^2 + 3x =$

8) $3x^2 - 4x - 2x =$

9) $7x + 5(4 - 3x) =$

10) $8x + 10(4x - 5) =$

11) $6(-4x - 5) + 8 =$

12) $4x^2 - (-9x) =$

13) $2x - 6 + 5x - 7x =$

14) $12x^2 - 6x - 8x^2 =$

15) $16x - 6 + 22x =$

16) $(-8x)(2x - 4) + 10x^2 =$

17) $6x - 5x(2 - 3x) =$

18) $4x - 2(2x + 1) + 3 =$

19) $4(-5x - 5) + 14x =$

20) $9x - 4x(2x + 1) =$

21) $8x + 3x(2 - 4x) =$

22) $7x(-2x - 7) + 5x =$

23) $6x + 10 - 7x^2 =$

24) $-3x(3x - 2) - 3 =$

25) $6x^2 - 8 + 4x - 3x^2 =$

26) $5x^2 + 2x - 3x^2 =$

27) $6x + 4x^2 - 9x^2 - 1 =$

28) $3 - x^2 + 9x^2 + 4x =$

29) $11x - 8x^2 - 3x - 3 =$

30) $5x^2 - 4x - 5x^2 =$

31) $13 - 11x^2 + 8x + 15x^2 =$

32) $2x - 7x - 2x^2 - 4 =$

Simplifying Polynomial Expressions

✎ *Simplify each polynomial.*

1) $(9x^5 - 3x^6) - (8x - 12x^6) =$ _____

2) $(6x^3 + 4x^2) - (3x^3 + 8x^2) =$ _____

3) $(11x^7 - 5x^5) - (4x^7 + 7x^5) =$ _____

4) $15x - 6x^4 + 4(2x^4 + 6x) =$ _____

5) $(4x^2 - 2) + 9(4x^5 - 6x^2) =$ _____

6) $(6x^5 + 3x) - 4(3x^3 - 6x^5) =$ _____

7) $5x^2 + x^5 - 2(3x^5 + 4x^2) =$ _____

8) $(4x^3 + 4x^2) - (6x^3 - x^2) =$ _____

9) $5x^8 - (3x^8 + 5x^2) + x^2 =$ _____

10) $3x^4 - 4(x^2 - x) - 9x =$ _____

11) $(3x^3 + x^5) - (2x^3 - 4x^5) =$ _____

12) $7x^6 + 9x^3 - 13x^6 - 20x^3 =$ _____

13) $6x^7 - 3x^2 - 3x^2 - 6x^7 =$ _____

14) $5x^6 - 2x^3 + 8x^3 - 6x^6 =$ _____

15) $12x^2 - 8x^3 - 4x^3 - 3x^2 =$ _____

16) $3x^3 - 14x + 2x^2 - 3x^3 =$ _____

Translate Phrases into an Algebraic Statement

✎ *Write an algebraic expression for each phrase.*

1) 12 multiplied by sum of 2 and x. _____

2) Subtract 15 from x. _____

3) 8 divided by z. _____

4) 18 decreased by $2y$. _____

5) Sum of y and 15 is 25. _____

6) The square of 6. _____

7) Sum of 6 and x raised to the fourth power. _____

8) The sum of fifteen and twice a number. _____

9) The difference between seventy–two and a. _____

10) The quotient of fourteen and three times a number. _____

11) The quotient of the square of x and 15. _____

12) The difference between x and 9 is 65. _____

13) 4 times x added to the square of y. _____

14) Subtract the product of $3a$ and $2b$ from 18. _____

The Distributive Property

✎ *Use the distributive property to simply each expression.*

1) $6(3 - 6x) =$

2) $8(4 + 7x) =$

3) $5(8x - 1) =$

4) $(7x - 3)(-4) =$

5) $(-6)(3x - 7) =$

6) $(12 - 6x)3 =$

7) $(-7)(6 - 3x) =$

8) $-2(-3 + 4x) =$

9) $(-10x + 3)(-2) =$

10) $(-12)(x + 7) =$

11) $-(9 - 5x) =$

12) $7(4 + 9x) =$

13) $9(4 - 3x) =$

14) $(-5x + 9)3 =$

15) $(2 - 7x)(-9) =$

16) $(-13)(3x - 2) =$

17) $(12 - 3x)2 =$

18) $4(3 + 5x) =$

19) $10(6x - 3) =$

20) $(-6x - 1)2 =$

21) $(4 - 8x)(-3) =$

22) $(-15)(3x - 2) =$

23) $(17 - 6x)3 =$

24) $(-6)(12x - 6) =$

25) $(4 - 2x)(-16) =$

26) $(-3)(2x - 2) =$

27) $(-3 - 7x)(-9) =$

28) $(-4)(2 - 8x) =$

29) $14(2x - 3) =$

30) $(-8x + 13)(-3) =$

31) $(-4)(3x - 4) + 2(x - 4) =$

32) $(-2)(x - 5) - (7 + 8x) =$

Evaluating One Variable Expressions

✎ **Evaluate each expression using the value given.**

1) $12 - x$, $x = 3$

2) $2x - 9$, $x = 2$

3) $3x - 4$, $x = 5$

4) $3x - 2$, $x = -4$

5) $4 - 2x$, $x = -5$

6) $2x - 8$, $x = 7$

7) $5x - 2$, $x = -1$

8) $x + (-6)$, $x = 9$

9) $2x + 4$, $x = -2$

10) $7x - 6$, $x = -4$

11) $7 + 10x - 9$, $x = -4$

12) $5 + 2x$, $x = 7$

13) $3x - 2$, $x = -6$

14) $4x - 2$, $x = 2$

15) $6x - 12$, $x = -3$

16) $14 - 8x$, $x = -4$

17) $9(3x - 4)$, $x = -3$

18) $7(-5x + 3)$, $x = 4$

19) $12x - 2x - 4$, $x = -2$

20) $(10x + 5) \div 15$, $x = -5$

21) $(2x - 4) \div 2$, $x = 6$

22) $8x - 2 + 6x$, $x = 4$

23) $(8 - 6x)(-3)$, $x = -5$

24) $13x^2 - 4x + 2$, $x = -5$

25) $2x^2 + 7x$, $x = -5$

26) $6x(1 - 2x)$, $x = -4$

27) $2x - 8 - 5x^2$, $x = 4$

28) $(-3)(7x - 9 + 5x)$, $x = -1$

29) $(-5) + \frac{3x}{7} + 4x$, $x = 14$

30) $(-3) + \frac{x}{2}$, $x = -4$

31) $\left(-\frac{8}{x}\right) - 9 + 5x$, $x = 4$

32) $\left(-\frac{15}{x}\right) - 10 + 9x$, $x = -5$

Evaluating Two Variables Expressions

✎ *Evaluate each expression using the values given.*

1) $6x - 3y$,

   $x = -2, y = 4$

2) $-10x + 3y$,

   $x = 3, y = 6$

3) $-3a + 8b$,

   $a = -2, b = 8$

4) $12x + 7 - 6y$,

   $x = -2, y = -1$

5) $6a + 3 - 4b$,

   $a = 8, b = -3$

6) $3(-3x + y)$,

   $x = 2, y = -7$

7) $14r - 6q + 1$,

   $r = -2, q = 3$

8) $6x \div 5y$,

   $x = -10, y = 3$

9) $6x + 6 - 7y$,

   $x = -5, y = -1$

10) $3a - (14 - 3b)$,

   $a = -2, b = 3$

11) $-3z + 4 - 6k$,

   $z = 3, k = -4$

12) $2xy - 12 - 4x$,

   $x = -2, y = -5$

13) $4x - 7y + 6$,

   $x = -6, y = -2$

14) $\left(-\frac{24}{x}\right) - 6xy$,

   $x = -2, y = -4$

15) $(-3)(-5a - 6b)$,

   $a = -7, b = -1$

16) $12 + 5x + y$,

   $x = -2, y = -12$

17) $12x - 6 - 9y$,

   $x = -2, y = -3$

18) $3 - 4(-3x + 2y)$,

   $x = -4, y = 5$

19) $6x - 12 - 7y$,

   $x = -5, y = 10$

20) $6a - (10a - 3b) - 1$,

   $a = -12, b = 7$

Combining like Terms

✎ *Simplify each expression.*

1) $12x - 6x - 5 =$

2) $3(7x + 8) =$

3) $12x - 9x + 1 =$

4) $(-9)(10x - 3) + 80x =$

5) $4x - 13x + 9 =$

6) $25x - 6 - 32x =$

7) $8 - (6x - 16) =$

8) $52x - 6 - 36x =$

9) $6x - 12 - 24x + 13 =$

10) $15x - 9x + 12 =$

11) $17 + 5x - 13 =$

12) $(-6x + 8)6 =$

13) $10 + 7x - 15x - 7 =$

14) $16(3x - 4x) + 2 =$

15) $3(4x - 14) - 9x =$

16) $14x - 8 - 19x =$

17) $3(5 - 4x) + 8x =$

18) $17x + 9 - 40x =$

19) $(-8x) - 13 + 9x =$

20) $(-12x) - 6 + 18x =$

21) $4(9x - 3) + 4x =$

22) $6(4 - 6x) - 14x =$

23) $-3x - (8 + 21x) =$

24) $(-12) - (5)(4x - 3) =$

25) $(-6)(7x - 2) - 4x =$

26) $-15x + 7 - 3x + 9x =$

27) $3(-5x + 9) - 18x =$

28) $-9x - 12 + 11x =$

29) $72x - 35x + 20 - 47x =$

30) $6(3x - 4x) + 12 =$

31) $13 - 14x - 11 + 19x =$

32) $4(-7x - 3x) + 42x =$

Answers

Simplifying Variable Expressions

1) $21x + 14$
2) $-12x + 20$
3) $-2x + 5$
4) $-6x^2 - 2x$
5) $7x^2 - x$
6) $3x^2 - 4x$
7) $-8x^2 + 3x$
8) $3x^2 - 6x$
9) $-8x + 20$
10) $48x - 50$

11) $-24x - 22$
12) $4x^2 + 9x$
13) -6
14) $4x^2 - 6x$
15) $38x - 6$
16) $-6x^2 + 32x$
17) $15x^2 - 4x$
18) 1
19) $-6x - 20$
20) $-8x^2 + 5x$
21) $-12x^2 + 14x$

22) $-14x^2 - 44x$
23) $-7x^2 + 6x + 10$
24) $-9x^2 + 6x - 3$
25) $3x^2 + 4x - 8$
26) $2x^2 + 2x$
27) $-5x^2 + 6x - 1$
28) $8x^2 + 4x + 3$
29) $-8x^2 + 8x - 3$
30) $-4x$
31) $4x^2 + 8x + 13$
32) $-2x^2 - 5x - 4$

Simplifying Polynomial Expressions

1) $9x^6 + 9x^5 - 8x$
2) $3x^3 - 4x^2$
3) $7x^7 - 12x^5$
4) $2x^4 + 39x$
5) $36x^5 - 50x^2 - 2$
6) $30x^5 - 12x^3 + 3x$
7) $-5x^5 - 3x^2$
8) $-2x^3 + 5x^2$

9) $2x^8 - 4x^2$
10) $3x^4 - 4x^2 - 8x$
11) $5x^5 + x^3$
12) $-6x^6 - 11x^3$
13) $-6x^2$
14) $-x^6 + 6x^3$
15) $-12x^3 + 9x^2$
16) $2x^2 - 14x$

Translate Phrases into an Algebraic Statement

1) $12(x + 2)$
2) $x - 15$
3) $\frac{8}{z}$
4) $18 - 2y$
5) $y + 15 = 25$

6) 6^2
7) $(x + 6)^4$
8) $15 + 2x$
9) $72 - a$
10) $\frac{14}{3x}$

11) $\frac{x^2}{15}$
12) $x - 9 = 65$
13) $4x + y^2$
14) $18 - (2a)(3b)$

The Distributive Property

1) $-36x + 18$
2) $56x + 32$
3) $40x - 5$
4) $-28x + 12$
5) $-18x + 42$
6) $-18x + 36$
7) $21x - 42$
8) $-8x + 6$

9) $20x - 6$
10) $-12x - 84$
11) $5x - 9$
12) $63x + 28$
13) $-27x + 36$
14) $-15x + 27$
15) $63x - 18$
16) $-39x + 26$

17) $-6x + 24$
18) $20x + 12$
19) $60x - 30$
20) $-12x - 2$
21) $24x - 12$
22) $-45x + 30$
23) $-18x + 51$
24) $-72x + 36$

25) $32x - 64$ 28) $32x - 8$ 31) $-10x + 8$

26) $-6x + 6$ 29) $28x - 42$ 32) $-10x + 3$

27) $63x + 27$ 30) $24x - 39$

Evaluating One Variables

1) 9   12) 19   23) -114

2) -5 13) -20 24) 347

3) 11   14) 6   25) 15

4) -14 15) -30 26) -216

5) 14   16) 46   27) -80

6) 6   17) -117 28) 63

7) -7 18) -119 29) 57

8) 3   19) -24 30) -5

9) 0   20) -3 31) 9

10) -34 21) 4   32) -52

11) -42 22) 54

Evaluating Two Variables

1) -24 9) -17 16) -10

2) -12 10) -11 17) -3

3) 70   11) 19   18) -85

4) -11 12) 16   19) -112

5) 63   13) -4 20) 68

6) -39 14) -36

7) -45 15) -123

8) -4

Combining like Terms

1) $6x - 5$ 12) $-36x + 48$ 22) $-50x + 24$

2) $21x + 24$ 13) $-8x + 3$ 23) $-24x - 8$

3) $3x + 1$ 14) $-16x + 2$ 24) $-20x + 3$

4) $-10x + 27$ 15) $3x - 42$ 25) $-46x + 12$

5) $-9x + 9$ 16) $-5x - 8$ 26) $-9x + 7$

6) $-7x - 6$ 17) $-4x + 15$ 27) $-33x + 27$

7) $-6x + 24$ 18) $-23x + 9$ 28) $2x - 12$

8) $16x - 6$ 19) $x - 13$ 29) $-10x + 20$

9) $-18x + 1$ 20) $6x - 6$ 30) $-6x + 12$

10) $6x + 12$ 21) $40x - 12$ 31) $5x + 2$

11) $5x + 4$ 32) $2x$

Chapter 6:

Equations and Inequalities

Topics that you'll practice in this chapter:

- ✓ One–Step Equations
- ✓ Multi–Step Equations
- ✓ Graphing Single–Variable Inequalities
- ✓ One–Step Inequalities
- ✓ Multi-Step Inequalities
- ✓ Systems of Equations
- ✓ Systems of Equations Word Problems
- ✓ Quadratic Equations

One-Step Equations

✏ *Solve each equation.*

1) $5x = 25, x =$ ____

2) $8x = 32, x =$ ____

3) $12x = 36, x =$ ____

4) $2x = 14, x =$ ____

5) $x - 3 = 5, x =$ ____

6) $x + 7 = 1, x =$ ____

7) $x - 9 = 13, x =$ ____

8) $x + 3 = 11, x =$ ____

9) $x - 6 = -11, x =$ ____

10) $-4 = 4 + x, x =$ ____

11) $x - 9 = 25, x =$ ____

12) $3 - x = -4, x =$ ____

13) $12 = -8 + x, x =$ ____

14) $x + 8 = 0, x =$ ____

15) $x + 17 = -2, x =$ ____

16) $17 = 21 - x, x =$ ____

17) $13 + x = -42, x =$ ____

18) $x - 6 = 4, x =$ ____

19) $10 = x - 8, x =$ ____

20) $x - 16 = -20, x =$ ____

21) $x - 7 = 5, x =$ ____

22) $x - 60 = -50, x =$ ____

23) $x - 15 = 27, x =$ ____

24) $-64 = x - 72, x =$ ____

25) $x - 19 = 11, x =$ ____

26) $39 = 3x, x =$ ____

27) $x - 20 = 18, x =$ ____

28) $x - 16 = 17, x =$ ____

29) $21 - x = -6, x =$ ____

30) $x + 4 = 19, x =$ ____

31) $14 - x = -3, x =$ ____

32) $x - 18 = -20, x =$ ____

Multi-Step Equations

✍ *Solve each equation.*

1) $3x + 6 = 12$

2) $-2x - 4 = 10$

3) $5x - 8 = 12$

4) $-4(3 - x) = 24$

5) $6x - 10 = 26$

6) $3x - 7 = 11$

7) $7x - 20 = 22$

8) $6x + 19 = 49$

9) $2x + 13 = 27$

10) $-5(3 + x) = 35$

11) $-6(4 + x) = -72$

12) $14 = -(x - 5)$

13) $3(4 - x) = 18$

14) $-27 = -(9x - 18)$

15) $3(2 + 3x) = -21$

16) $5(x - 11) = 35$

17) $-72 = 12x - 12$

18) $5x + 20 = -x - 16$

19) $3(1 + 3x) = -42$

20) $17 - 3x = -7 + x$

21) $13 - 2x = 28 + 3x$

22) $7 + 4x = -8 + x$

23) $33 = (-5x) - 12$

24) $64 = 8x - 8 - 2x$

25) $-18 = -3x - 4 + 5x$

26) $2x - 20 = -38 + 5x$

27) $9x - 60 = 4x - 5$

28) $-15 - 5x = 3(2 - 4x)$

29) $x + 30 = -2(3 - 2x)$

30) $15x - 28 = 10x - 43$

31) $-11x - 4 = -5(12 + 3x)$

32) $-7x - 65 = 6x + 52$

Graphing Single-Variable Inequalities

 Draw a graph for each inequality.

1) $x > 5$
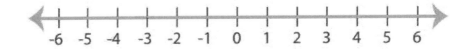

2) $x < 4$
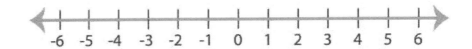

3) $x > -6$

4) $x \geq 1$

5) $x < 7$
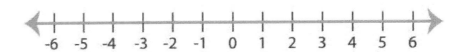

6) $x \geq -3$

7) $x \leq 2$

8) $x > -7$

One-Step Inequalities

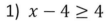 *Solve each inequality and graph it.*

1) $x - 4 \geq 4$

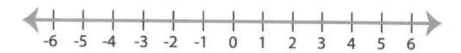

2) $2x + 3 \leq 4$

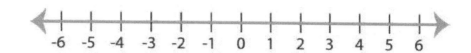

3) $3x + 1 \geq 7$

4) $6 - x \leq 2$

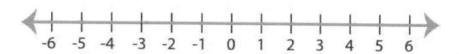

5) $3x - 5 \leq 13$

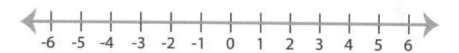

6) $5x - 4 > 6$

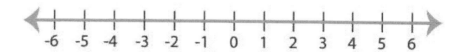

7) $11x \leq 33$

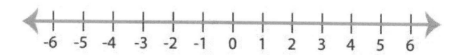

8) $4x + 2 \geq 14$

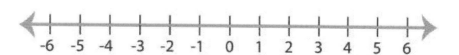

Multi-Step Inequalities

✎ *Solve each inequality.*

1) $5x - 4 \leq 16$

2) $6 - 2x \leq 24$

3) $4x + 8 \leq 24$

4) $2x - 1 \geq -9$

5) $3x - 7 \geq 8$

6) $6x - 7 > 17$

7) $3x - 5 \leq 13$

8) $-9 + 4x \geq 7$

9) $4(x - 2) \leq 24$

10) $4x - 15 \leq -3$

11) $2x + 7 < 23$

12) $9x + 18 < 27$

13) $21 - 7x \geq -70$

14) $2 + 2x < 18$

15) $5 + 7x \geq 68$

16) $3 - 2x < 9$

17) $6x - 5 < 31$

18) $2(4 - 2x) \geq 0$

19) $-2(5 + 3x) < 12$

20) $13 - 9x \geq -59$

21) $-4(2x - 6) > 16$

22) $\dfrac{5x - 1}{3} \geq 13$

23) $\dfrac{2x + 9}{3} \leq 17$

24) $\dfrac{7x - 17}{6} < 10$

25) $6 + \dfrac{x}{2} < 4$

26) $\dfrac{7x}{6} - 9 < 5$

27) $\dfrac{6x - 9}{9} > 11$

28) $19 + \dfrac{x}{10} < 41$

Systems of Equations

✍️ **Solve each system of equations.**

1) $4x - 3y = -30$ $x =$ ____
   $2x + y = -10$ $y =$ ____

2) $4x + 3y = -10$ $x =$ ____
   $-2x + 4y = 38$ $y =$ ____

3) $5x + 2y = 4$ $x =$ ____
   $-3x + 4y = -18$ $y =$ ____

4) $7x + 4y = -29$ $x =$ ____
   $5x - 6y = -3$ $y =$ ____

5) $11x + 2y = -3$ $x =$ ____
   $3x - 4y = -19$ $y =$ ____

6) $2x + 7y = 22$ $x =$ ____
   $x - 3y = -15$ $y =$ ____

7) $-2x + y = -12$ $x =$ ____
   $5x - 4y = 27$ $y =$ ____

8) $-x + 3y = 12$ $x =$ ____
   $2x + 3y = 3$ $y =$ ____

9) $2x - y = 42$ $x =$ ____
   $x + y = 3$ $y =$ ____

10) $2x + 3y = 0$ $x =$ ____
   $4x - y = -42$ $y =$ ____

11) $-3x + 7y = 57$ $x =$ ____
   $2x - y = -16$ $y =$ ____

12) $8x + 2y = 10$ $x =$ ____
   $7x - y = -16$ $y =$ ____

13) $4x + 5y = -4$ $x =$ ____
   $6x - 2y = 32$ $y =$ ____

14) $2x + 4y = 4$ $x =$ ____
   $3x + 8y = 2$ $y =$ ____

15) $x + 7y = 17$ $x =$ ____
   $3x - 14y = 16$ $y =$ ____

16) $3x - y = -51$ $x =$ ____
   $x + 2y = 18$ $y =$ ____

Systems of Equations Word Problems

✎ *Solve each word problem.*

1) Tickets to a movie cost $6 for adults and $4 for students. A group of friends purchased 14 tickets for $64.00. How many adults ticket did they buy? _____

2) At a store, Eva bought five shirts and four hats for $180.00. Nicole bought three same shirts and three same hats for $114.00. What is the price of each shirt? _____

3) A farmhouse shelters 12 animals, some are pigs, and some are ducks. Altogether there are 40 legs. How many pigs are there? _____

4) A class of 280 students went on a field trip. They took 22 vehicles, some cars and some buses. If each car holds 4 students and each bus hold 20 students, how many buses did they take? _____

5) A theater is selling tickets for a performance. Mr. Smith purchased 12 senior tickets and 6 child tickets for $144 for his friends and family. Mr. Jackson purchased 8 senior tickets and 5 child tickets for $102. What is the price of a senior ticket? $_____

6) The difference of two numbers is 14. Their sum is 20. What is the bigger number? $_____

7) The sum of the digits of a certain two-digit number is 13. Reversing its digits increase the number by 27. What is the number? _____

8) The difference of two numbers is 12. Their sum is 50. What are the numbers? _____

9) The length of a rectangle is 5 meters greater than 4 times the width. The perimeter of rectangle is 60 meters. What is the length of the rectangle? _____

10) Jim has 62 nickels and dimes totaling $5.30. How many nickels does he have? _____

Quadratic Equation

✍ Multiply.

1) $(x - 6)(x + 1) =$ _____

2) $(x - 5)(x + 4) =$ _____

3) $(x - 7)(x + 3) =$ _____

4) $(x - 6)(x - 8) =$ _____

5) $(x - 3)(x - 5) =$ _____

6) $(3x + 6)(x + 4) =$ _____

7) $(2x + 8)(x + 2) =$ _____

8) $(2x - 4)(2x + 4) =$ _____

9) $(2x - 4)(3x + 1) =$ _____

10) $(2x - 6)(4x + 3) =$ _____

✍ Factor each expression.

11) $x^2 + 2x - 8 =$ _____

12) $x^2 - x - 20 =$ _____

13) $x^2 + x - 56 =$ _____

14) $x^2 - 8x - 9 =$ _____

15) $x^2 + 5x - 24 =$ _____

16) $3x^2 + 7x + 2 =$ _____

17) $4x^2 - 1 =$ _____

18) $20x^2 + 19x + 3 =$ _____

19) $5x^2 - 37x - 24 =$ _____

20) $7x^2 + 20x - 3 =$ _____

✍ Solve each equation.

21) $(x + 7)(x - 5) = 0$

22) $(x + 4)(x + 2) = 0$

23) $(2x + 8)(x - 2) = 0$

24) $(3x + 12)(2x - 10) = 0$

25) $12x^2 - 60x - 72 = 0$

26) $2x^2 - 12x + 18 = 0$

27) $3x^2 - 3x - 12 = 6$

28) $4x^2 + 16x + 10 = -2$

29) $10x^2 - 40x + 40 = 0$

30) $8x^2 + 24x = 80$

Answers

One–Step Equations

1) 5	12) 7	23) 42
2) 4	13) 20	24) 8
3) 3	14) −8	25) 30
4) 7	15) −19	26) 13
5) 8	16) 4	27) 38
6) −6	17) −55	28) 33
7) 22	18) 10	29) 27
8) 8	19) 18	30) 15
9) −5	20) −4	31) 17
10) −8	21) 12	32) −2
11) 34	22) 10	

Multi–Step Equations

1) 2	12) −9	23) −9
2) −7	13) −2	24) 12
3) 4	14) 5	25) −7
4) 9	15) −3	26) 6
5) 6	16) 18	27) 11
6) 6	17) −5	28) 3
7) 6	18) −6	29) 12
8) 5	19) −5	30) −3
9) 7	20) 6	31) −14
10) −10	21) −3	32) −9
11) 8	22) −5	

Graphing Single–Variable Inequalities

1)
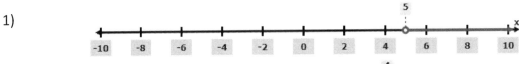

2)
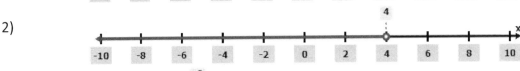

3)

4)

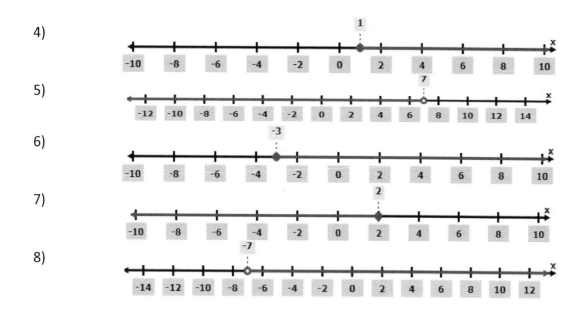

5)

6)

7)

8)

One–Step Inequalities

1)

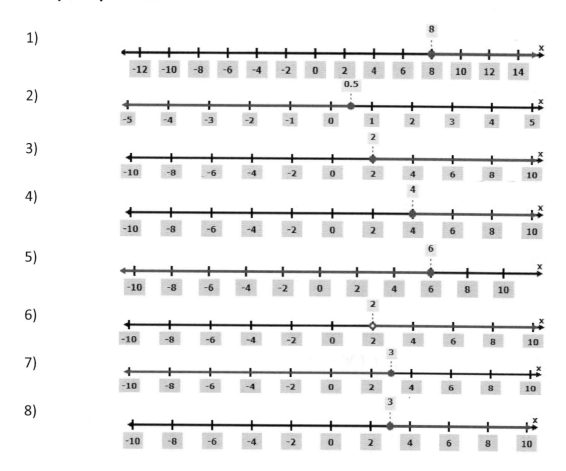

2)

3)

4)

5)

6)

7)

8)

Multi-Step Inequalities

1) $x \leq 4$
2) $x \geq -9$
3) $x \leq 4$
4) $x \geq -4$
5) $x \geq 5$
6) $x > 4$
7) $x \leq 6$
8) $x \geq 4$
9) $x \leq 8$
10) $x \leq 3$

11) $x < 8$
12) $x < 1$
13) $x \leq 13$
14) $x < 8$
15) $x \geq 9$
16) $x > -3$
17) $x < 6$
18) $x \leq 2$
19) $x > -\frac{11}{3}$

20) $x \leq 8$
21) $x < 1$
22) $x \geq 8$
23) $x \leq 21$
24) $x < 11$
25) $x < -4$
26) $x < 12$
27) $x > 18$
28) $x < 220$

Systems of Equations

1) $x = -6, y = 2$
2) $x = -7, y = 6$
3) $x = 2, y = -3$
4) $x = -3, y = -2$
5) $x = -1, y = 4$
6) $x = -3, y = 4$

7) $x = 7, y = 2$
8) $x = -3, y = 3$
9) $x = 15, y = -12$
10) $x = -9, y = 6$
11) $x = -5, y = 6$
12) $x = -1, y = 9$

13) $x = 4, y = -4$
14) $x = 6, y = -2$
15) $x = 10, y = 1$
16) $x = -12, y = 15$

Systems of Equations Word Problems

1) 4
2) $28
3) 8
4) 12

5) $9
6) 12
7) 58
8) 31,19

9) 25 $meters$
10) 44

Quadratic Equations

1) $x^2 - 5x - 6$
2) $x^2 - x - 20$
3) $x^2 - 4x - 21$
4) $x^2 - 14x + 48$
5) $x^2 - 8x + 15$
6) $3x^2 + 18x + 24$
7) $2x^2 + 12x + 16$
8) $4x^2 - 16$
9) $6x^2 - 10x - 4$
10) $8x^2 - 18x - 18$

11) $(x + 4)(x - 2)$
12) $(x + 4)(x - 5)$
13) $(x - 7)(x + 8)$
14) $(x + 1)(x - 9)$
15) $(x + 8)(x - 3)$
16) $(3x + 1)(x + 2)$
17) $(2x - 1)(2x + 1)$
18) $(4x + 3)(5x + 1)$
19) $(5x + 3)(x - 8)$
20) $(7x - 1)(x + 3)$
21) $x = -7, x = 5$

22) $x = -4, x = -2$
23) $x = -4, x = 2$
24) $x = -4, x = 5$
25) $x = -1, x = 6$
26) $x = 3, x = 3$
27) $x = 3, x = -2$
28) $x = -3, x = -1$
29) $x = 2, x = 2$
30) $x = 2, x = -5$

Chapter 7:

Linear Functions

Topics that you'll practice in this chapter:

- ✓ Finding Slope
- ✓ Graphing Lines Using Line Equation
- ✓ Writing Linear Equations
- ✓ Graphing Linear Inequalities
- ✓ Finding Midpoint
- ✓ Finding Distance of Two Points

Finding Slope

✎ **Find the slope of each line.**

1) $y = 3x - 4$

2) $y = -7x + 6$

3) $y = -2x + 4$

4) $y = -3x + 3$

5) $y = 8 - 7x$

6) $y = 1 - 2x$

7) $y = 7x + 10$

8) $y = 9x + 5$

9) $y = -\frac{3}{4}x + 3$

10) $y = \frac{1}{2}x + 8$

11) $y = \frac{7}{5}x + 2$

12) $2y = -6x + 7$

13) $-5x + 3y = 1$

14) $8x + 4y = 12$

15) $10y - 15x = -20$

16) $6y - 30x = 45$

✎ **Find the slope of the line through each pair of points.**

17) $(5, -11), (-3, 13)$

18) $(-2, 6), (0, -2)$

19) $(5, -4), (1, 4)$

20) $(1, -5), (9, 7)$

21) $(3, 4), (1, -6)$

22) $(-3, -6), (1, 10)$

23) $(1, -4), (5, 2)$

24) $(2, 1), (3, 5)$

25) $(3, 3), (-1, -7)$

26) $(2, -10), (4, 0)$

27) $(0, 1), (1, 7)$

28) $(3, -7), (7, 7)$

Graphing Lines Using Line Equation

✏ *Sketch the graph of each line.*

1) $y = \frac{3}{2}x + 1$

2) $y = -2x - 1$

3) $2x + 3y = 3$

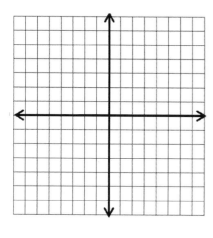
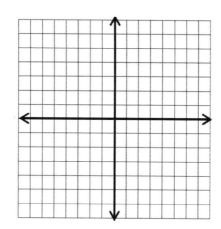
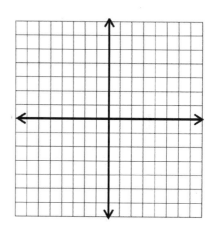

4) $3x - 4y = 10$

5) $5x - y = 1$

6) $2x - 5y = 5$

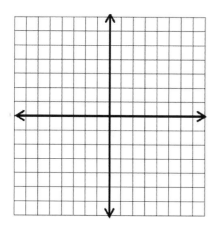
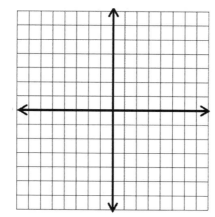
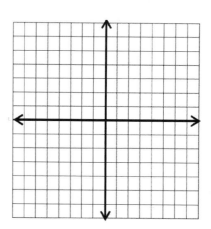

Writing Linear Equations

✎ **Write the equation of the line through the given points.**

1) through: $(3, -1), (1, 5)$

2) through: $(-3, 3), (1, 1)$

3) through: $(-5, 2), (-1, 6)$

4) through: $(4, -2), (0, 6)$

5) through: $(3, 5), (-5, -7)$

6) through: $(0, 5), (-4, 1)$

7) through: $(6, -6), (2, 2)$

8) through: $(1, -2), (3, 2)$

9) through: $(5, 5), (3, 7)$

10) through: $(2, 1), (-1, -11)$

11) through: $(4, -3), (-2, 9)$

12) through: $(-6, 6), (-2, 20)$

13) through: $(9, -1), (-1, -11)$

14) through: $(3, 7), (-3, -5)$

15) through: $(2, 4), (4, -8)$

16) through: $(7, 2), (3, 8)$

✎ **Solve each problem.**

17) What is the equation of a line with slope 5 and intercept 6? _____

18) What is the equation of a line with slope -7 and intercept 2? _____

19) What is the equation of a line with slope -3 and passes through point $(2, 3)$?

_____

20) What is the equation of a line with slope -4 and passes through point $(-1, 5)$?

_____

21) The slope of a line is 5 and it passes through point $(-3, 2)$. What is the equation of the

line? _____

22) The slope of a line is -6 and it passes through point $(4, 6)$. What is the equation of the

line? _____

Graphing Linear Inequalities

✎ *Sketch the graph of each linear inequality.*

1) $y > 4x + 3$

2) $y < -6x - 2$

3) $y \leq -\frac{1}{3}x + 2$

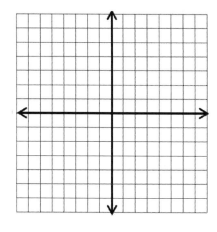
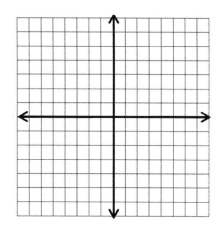
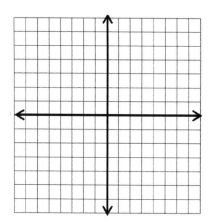

4) $5y \geq 3 + 4x$

5) $3y < 4x - 2$

6) $2y \leq -5x - 3$

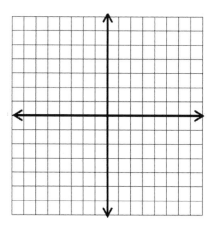
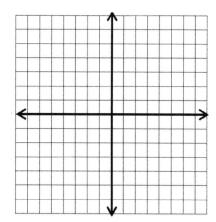
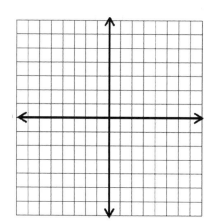

Finding Midpoint

✍ ***Find the midpoint of the line segment with the given endpoints.***

1) $(3, 10), (5, 8)$

2) $(7, 4), (9, 0)$

3) $(-6, 2), (-4, 8)$

4) $(4, 10), (-2, 12)$

5) $(0, 6), (2, 20)$

6) $(12, 5), (4, -7)$

7) $(5, 10), (-5, 8)$

8) $(-4, 8), (2, 2)$

9) $(12, 7), (2, -9)$

10) $(5, 2), (11, -8)$

11) $(13, -2), (-1, 8)$

12) $(1, 1), (7, 7)$

13) $(-9, 3), (5, 9)$

14) $(2, 2), (8, 12)$

15) $(-4, 3), (12, -1)$

16) $(3, -3), (-3, 3)$

17) $(14, 9), (6, 1)$

18) $(6, 8), (-2, -6)$

19) $(12, 11), (-4, 5)$

20) $(17, 15), (1, 3)$

21) $(19, -5), (7, -5)$

22) $(8, 3), (6, 15)$

23) $(5, -11), (3, -7)$

24) $(2, 2), (12, 14)$

✍ ***Solve each problem.***

25) One endpoint of a line segment is $(3, 3)$ and the midpoint of the line segment is $(-10, 2)$. What is the other endpoint? _____

26) One endpoint of a line segment is $(-2, 1)$ and the midpoint of the line segment is $(-6, 5)$. What is the other endpoint? _____

27) One endpoint of a line segment is $(4, -3)$ and the midpoint of the line segment is $(9, 3)$. What is the other endpoint? _____

Finding Distance of Two Points

✍ **Find the distance between each pair of points.**

1) $(10, 17), (2, 2)$

2) $(-15, 7), (5, -14)$

3) $(6, 7), (3, 3)$

4) $(-9, 13), (-3, 5)$

5) $(5, 9), (20, -27)$

6) $(19, 15), (-1, -6)$

7) $(12, -13), (0, 3)$

8) $(24, 17), (8, -13)$

9) $(-6, -10), (3, 2)$

10) $(11, 14), (-9, 35)$

11) $(19, -32), (9, -8)$

12) $(-18, 0), (2, 48)$

13) $(14, -16), (6, -1)$

14) $(32, 16), (17, -20)$

15) $(15, -10), (7, 5)$

16) $(-13, 11), (-3, -13)$

17) $(-4, 7), (2, 15)$

18) $(-9, -3), (11, 18)$

19) $(-19, 18), (2, -10)$

20) $(-4, 8), (6, -16)$

✍ **Solve each problem.**

21) Triangle ABC is a right triangle on the coordinate system and its vertices are $(-3, 2)$, $(-3, 6)$, and $(0, 2)$. What is the area of triangle ABC? _____

22) Three vertices of a triangle on a coordinate system are $(3, 10)$, $(18, 2)$, and $(3, 2)$. What is the perimeter of the triangle? _____

23) Four vertices of a rectangle on a coordinate system are $(4, 5)$, $(4, -1)$, $(9, 5)$, and $(9, -1)$. What is its perimeter? _____

Answers

Finding Slope

1) 3
2) −7
3) −2
4) −3
5) −7
6) −2
7) 7
8) 9
9) $\frac{-3}{4}$
10) $\frac{1}{2}$

11) $\frac{7}{5}$
12) −3
13) $\frac{5}{3}$
14) −2
15) $\frac{3}{2}$
16) 5
17) −3
18) −4
19) −2

20) $\frac{3}{2}$
21) 5
22) 4
23) $\frac{3}{2}$
24) 4
25) $\frac{5}{2}$
26) 5
27) 6
28) $\frac{7}{2}$

Graphing Lines Using Line Equation

1) $y = \frac{3}{2}x + 1$

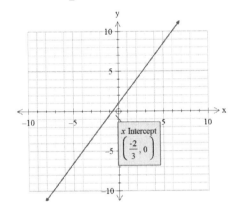

2) $y = -2x - 1$

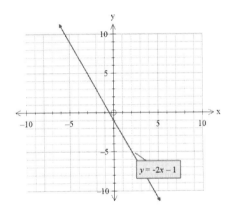

3) $2x + 3y = 3$

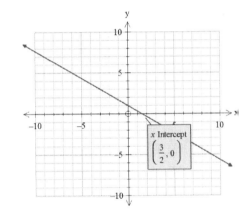

4) $3x - 4y = 10$

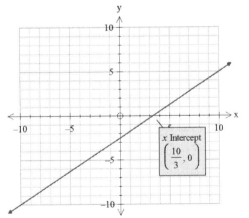

5) $5x - y = 1$

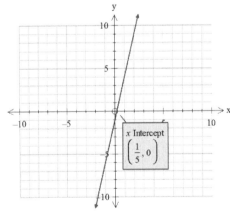

6) $2x - 5y = 5$

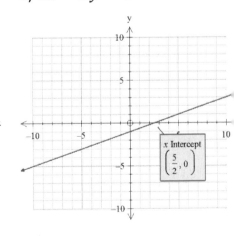

Writing Linear Equations

1) $y = -3x + 8$

2) $y = -\frac{1}{2}x + \frac{3}{2}$

3) $y = x + 7$

4) $y = -2x + 6$

5) $y = \frac{3}{2}x + \frac{1}{2}$

6) $y = x + 5$

7) $y = -2x + 6$

8) $y = 2x - 4$

9) $y = -x + 10$

10) $y = 4x - 7$

11) $y = -2x + 5$

12) $y = \frac{7}{2}x + 27$

13) $y = x - 10$

14) $y = 2x + 1$

15) $y = -6x + 16$

16) $y = -\frac{3}{2}x + \frac{25}{2}$

17) $y = 5x + 6$

18) $y = -7x + 2$

19) $y = -3x + 9$

20) $y = -4x + 1$

21) $y = 5x + 17$

22) $y = -6x + 30$

Graphing Linear Inequalities

1) $y > 4x + 3$

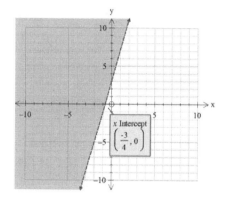

2) $y < -6x - 2$

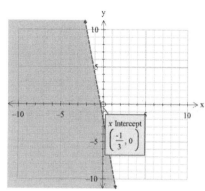

3) $y \leq -\frac{1}{3}x + 2$

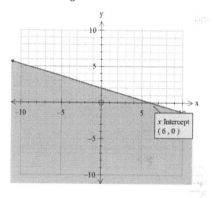

4) $5y \geq 3 + 4x$

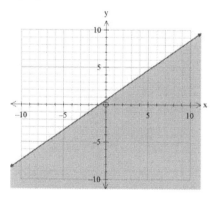

5) $3y < 4x - 2$

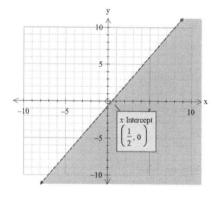

6) $2y \leq -5x - 3$

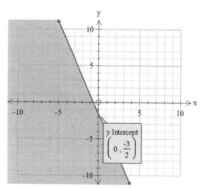

Finding Midpoint

1) $(4, 9)$

2) $(8, 2)$

3) $(-5, 5)$

4) $(1, 11)$

5) $(1, 13)$

6) $(8, -1)$

7) $(0, 9)$

8) $(-1, 5)$

9) $(7, -1)$

10) $(8, -3)$

11) $(6, 3)$

12) $(4, 4)$

13) $(-2,6)$

14) $(5,7)$

15) $(4,1)$

16) $(0,0)$

17) $(10,5)$

18) $(2,1)$

19) $(4,8)$

20) $(9,9)$

21) $(13,-5)$

22) $(7,9)$

23) $(4,-9)$

24) $(7,8)$

25) $(-23,1)$

26) $(-10,9)$

27) $(14,9)$

Finding Distance of Two Points

1) 17

2) 29

3) 5

4) 10

5) 39

6) 29

7) 20

8) 34

9) 15

10) 29

11) 26

12) 52

13) 17

14) 39

15) 17

16) 26

17) 10

18) 29

19) 35

20) 26

21) 6 *square units*

22) 40 *units*

23) 22 *units*

Chapter 8:

Exponents and Radicals

Topics that you'll practice in this chapter:

- ✓ Multiplication Property of Exponents
- ✓ Zero and Negative Exponents
- ✓ Division Property of Exponents
- ✓ Powers of Products and Quotients
- ✓ Negative Exponents and Negative Bases
- ✓ Scientific Notation
- ✓ Square Roots

Multiplication Property of Exponents

✎ *Simplify and write the answer in exponential form.*

1) $7 \times 7^5 =$

2) $11^2 \times 11 =$

3) $8^6 \times 8^3 =$

4) $3^6 \times 3^4 =$

5) $10^7 \times 10^6 \times 10 =$

6) $5 \times 5^6 \times 5^3 =$

7) $12^4 \times 12^3 \times 12 \times 12 =$

8) $6x \times x^2 =$

9) $5x^8 \times 2x^2 =$

10) $6x^5 \times 3x^2 =$

11) $3x^4 \times x^2 \times x^8 =$

12) $2x \times 8x =$

13) $5x^3 \times 2x^6 =$

14) $5x^3 \times x^2 =$

15) $3x^2 \times 3x^2 \times 3x^2 =$

16) $7x^3 \times 2x^2 =$

17) $5x^6 \times 6x =$

18) $3x \times 4x^5 =$

19) $6x^7 \times 4x^7 =$

20) $(-2)yx^3 \times 3y =$

21) $6x^2y \times (-2)y^3x^5 =$

22) $2y^3x^3 \times (-y^2x^4) =$

23) $7y^6x^2 \times 4x^4y^2 =$

24) $2x^4 \times 3x^2y^6 =$

25) $2x^2y^8 \times 5x^7y^2 =$

26) $x^6y^2 \times 4xy^5 =$

27) $6xy^8 \times 2x^2y^4 =$

28) $8x^2y^2 \times 7x^4y^5 =$

29) $2x \times y^4x^3 \times y^9 =$

30) $yx^5 \times 6y^4x^3 \times 3xy =$

31) $2y^3x^2 \times 2y^2x \times 2xy^6 =$

32) $8x^2 \times y^4x^2 \times 6yx^8 =$

Zero and Negative Exponents

✎ *Evaluate the following expressions.*

1) $3^{-1} =$

2) $5^{-1} =$

3) $11^{-2} =$

4) $8^{-3} =$

5) $5^{-3} =$

6) $7^{-2} =$

7) $9^{-1} =$

8) $15^{0} =$

9) $4^{-3} =$

10) $6^{-3} =$

11) $16^{-2} =$

12) $30^{-2} =$

13) $17^{-1} =$

14) $14^{-2} =$

15) $19^{-2=}$

16) $18^{-1} =$

17) $6^{-1} =$

18) $15^{-1} =$

19) $21^{-1} =$

20) $3^{-4} =$

21) $8^{-2} =$

22) $20^{-1} =$

23) $12^{-2} =$

24) $2^{-7} =$

25) $13^{-1} =$

26) $35^{-1} =$

27) $27^{-1} =$

28) $3^{-6} =$

29) $10^{-4} =$

30) $9^{-3} =$

31) $\left(\frac{1}{5}\right)^{-3}$

32) $\left(\frac{1}{4}\right)^{-3} =$

33) $\left(\frac{2}{3}\right)^{-1} =$

34) $\left(\frac{3}{7}\right)^{-3} =$

35) $\left(\frac{1}{2}\right)^{-5} =$

36) $\left(\frac{2}{9}\right)^{-1} =$

37) $\left(\frac{3}{11}\right)^{-1} =$

38) $\left(\frac{1}{6}\right)^{-2} =$

39) $\left(\frac{5}{6}\right)^{-2} =$

40) $\left(\frac{1}{3}\right)^{-4} =$

41) $\left(\frac{3}{10}\right)^{-2} =$

42) $\left(\frac{5}{9}\right)^{-1} =$

Division Property of Exponents

✏ *Simplify.*

1) $\dfrac{9^5}{9^4} =$

2) $\dfrac{5^3}{5^4} =$

3) $\dfrac{7^3}{7} =$

4) $\dfrac{8}{8^2} =$

5) $\dfrac{2x}{x^2} =$

6) $\dfrac{6 \times 6^5}{6^3 \times 6^3} =$

7) $\dfrac{12^5}{12^3} =$

8) $\dfrac{9 \times 9^3}{9^3 \times 9^2} =$

9) $\dfrac{4^6 \times 4^4}{4^2 \times 4^5} =$

10) $\dfrac{8x}{12x^2} =$

11) $\dfrac{5x^5}{7x^4} =$

12) $\dfrac{8x^4}{7x^3} =$

13) $\dfrac{15x^2}{11xy^3} =$

14) $\dfrac{3xy^2}{7x^2y^3} =$

15) $\dfrac{4x^6}{5x^4} =$

16) $\dfrac{13x^3y^5}{10x^3} =$

17) $\dfrac{9x^5}{8x^4y^3} =$

18) $\dfrac{15x^3}{21x^5} =$

19) $\dfrac{24x^3y^2}{30x^4y^2} =$

20) $\dfrac{21x^7}{25x^6} =$

21) $\dfrac{6x^{-9}}{10x^{-10}} =$

Powers of Products and Quotients

✎ *Simplify.*

1) $(6^3)^5 =$

2) $(4^2)^4 =$

3) $(3 \times 3^2)^3 =$

4) $(8 \times 8^2)^5 =$

5) $(6^2 \times 6^4)^2 =$

6) $(10^2 \times 10^3)^3 =$

7) $(3 \times 3^3)^3 =$

8) $(4^3)^5 =$

9) $(8x^3)^2 =$

10) $(2x^3y^5)^3 =$

11) $(3x^2y^3)^2 =$

12) $(4x^4y^5)^3 =$

13) $(2x^3y^4)^5 =$

14) $(4x^3y^4)^3 =$

15) $(2x^2x)^5 =$

16) $(5x^4x^3)^3 =$

17) $(3x^5y^2)^4 =$

18) $(2x^2x^4)^6 =$

19) $(6x^7y)^2 =$

20) $(7x^9y^5)^2 =$

21) $(6x^3y^4)^3 =$

22) $(2x^2y^3)^8 =$

23) $(5x \cdot 2y^5)^3 =$

24) $\left(\frac{5x}{x^3}\right)^3 =$

25) $\left(\frac{x^6y^7}{x^5y^4}\right)^2 =$

26) $\left(\frac{16x}{8x^3}\right)^2 =$

27) $\left(\frac{2x^5}{x^4y^3}\right)^3 =$

28) $\left(\frac{xy^6}{x^2y^2}\right)^{-4} =$

29) $\left(\frac{3xy^5}{x^6}\right)^{-2} =$

30) $\left(\frac{x^2y^3}{10xy^4}\right)^{-1} =$

Negative Exponents and Negative Bases

✎ *Simplify.*

1) $-9^{-2} =$

2) $-3^{-3} =$

3) $-5^{-1} =$

4) $-x^{-2} =$

5) $(-2x)^{-2} =$

6) $-3x^{-7} =$

7) $-4x^{-2} =$

8) $(-5x)^{-2}y^{-1} =$

9) $12x^{-3}y^{-2} =$

10) $11a^{-3}b^{-2} =$

11) $-6x^4y^{-5} =$

12) $-\dfrac{20x}{x^{-2}} =$

13) $-\dfrac{15b}{a^{-3}} =$

14) $\left(-\dfrac{1}{2}\right)^{-4} =$

15) $\left(-\dfrac{1}{5}\right)^{-3} =$

16) $-\dfrac{10}{a^{-2}b^{-4}} =$

17) $-\dfrac{7x}{x^{-6}} =$

18) $-\dfrac{a^{-3}}{ab^{-4}} =$

19) $-\dfrac{6}{x^{-4}} =$

20) $\dfrac{2b}{-3c^{-5}} =$

21) $\dfrac{6ab}{a^{-4}b^{-5}} =$

22) $-\dfrac{12n^{-4}}{16p^{-4}} =$

23) $\dfrac{5ab^{-3}}{-4c^{-3}} =$

24) $\left(-\dfrac{4a}{3c}\right)^{-1} =$

25) $\left(-\dfrac{2x^2}{6yz^2}\right)^{-2} =$

26) $\dfrac{5ab^{-3}}{-4c^{-6}} =$

27) $\left(-\dfrac{2x^2}{x^{-1}}\right)^{-2} =$

28) $\left(-\dfrac{x^{-3}}{3x^3}\right)^{-2} =$

29) $\left(-\dfrac{3x^{-3}}{x^{-5}}\right)^{-1} =$

Scientific Notation

✏️ **Write each number in scientific notation.**

1) $0.211 =$

2) $0.005 =$

3) $8.5 =$

4) $45 =$

5) $900 =$

6) $0.009 =$

7) $32 =$

8) $3,200 =$

9) $11,100 =$

10) $71,000 =$

11) $90,000,000 =$

12) $0.0000008 =$

13) $541,000,000 =$

14) $0.0000045 =$

15) $0.000000765 =$

16) $132,000,000 =$

17) $49,000 =$

18) $53,000,000 =$

19) 0.00000356

20) $0.000000019 =$

✏️ **Write each number in standard notation.**

21) $7 \times 10^{-3} =$

22) $6 \times 10^{-5} =$

23) $3.7 \times 10^{5} =$

24) $4.56 \times 10^{-3} =$

25) $3.6 \times 10^{-4} =$

26) $4.2 \times 10^{5} =$

27) $7 \times 10^{6} =$

28) $2.1 \times 10^{3} =$

29) $8 \times 10^{-9} =$

30) $7.56 \times 10^{-7} =$

Square Roots

✍ **Find the value each square root.**

1) $\sqrt{441} =$ ____

2) $\sqrt{529} =$ ____

3) $\sqrt{729} =$ ____

4) $\sqrt{169} =$ ____

5) $\sqrt{961} =$ ____

6) $\sqrt{289} =$ ____

7) $\sqrt{1089} =$ ____

8) $\sqrt{2025} =$ ____

9) $\sqrt{484} =$ ____

10) $\sqrt{144} =$ ____

11) $\sqrt{1156} =$ ____

12) $\sqrt{784} =$ ____

13) $\sqrt{1369} =$ ____

14) $\sqrt{0} =$ ____

15) $\sqrt{1600} =$ ____

16) $\sqrt{1681} =$ ____

17) $\sqrt{1764} =$ ____

18) $\sqrt{2500} =$ ____

19) $\sqrt{405} =$ ____

20) $\sqrt{2166} =$ ____

21) $\sqrt{147} =$ ____

22) $\sqrt{448} =$ ____

23) $\sqrt{3600} =$ ____

24) $\sqrt{600} =$ ____

✍ **Evaluate.**

25) $\sqrt{3} \times \sqrt{27} =$ _____

26) $\sqrt{16} \times \sqrt{81} =$ _____

27) $\sqrt{36} \times \sqrt{49} =$ _____

28) $\sqrt{5} \times \sqrt{125} =$ _____

29) $\sqrt{64} \times \sqrt{49} =$ _____

30) $\sqrt{21} \times \sqrt{21} =$ _____

31) $\sqrt{8} + \sqrt{2} =$ _____

32) $\sqrt{125} + 2\sqrt{5} =$ _____

33) $7\sqrt{2} - 5\sqrt{2} =$ _____

34) $5\sqrt{5} \times 6\sqrt{5} =$ _____

35) $7\sqrt{7} \times 5\sqrt{7} =$ _____

36) $4\sqrt{3} - \sqrt{48} =$ _____

Answers

Multiplication Property of Exponents

1) 7^6
2) 11^3
3) 8^9
4) 3^{10}
5) 10^{14}
6) 5^{10}
7) 12^9
8) $6x^3$
9) $10x^{10}$
10) $18x^7$
11) $3x^{14}$

12) $16x^2$
13) $10x^9$
14) $5x^5$
15) $27x^6$
16) $14x^5$
17) $30x^7$
18) $12x^6$
19) $24x^{14}$
20) $-6x^3y^2$
21) $-12x^7y^4$
22) $-2x^7y^5$

23) $28x^6y^8$
24) $6x^6y^6$
25) $10x^9y^{10}$
26) $4x^7y^7$
27) $12x^3y^{12}$
28) $56x^6y^7$
29) $2x^4y^{13}$
30) $18x^9y^6$
31) $8x^4y^{11}$
32) $48x^{12}y^5$

Zero and Negative Exponents

1) $\frac{1}{3}$
2) $\frac{1}{5}$
3) $\frac{1}{121}$
4) $\frac{1}{512}$
5) $\frac{1}{125}$
6) $\frac{1}{49}$
7) $\frac{1}{9}$
8) 1
9) $\frac{1}{64}$
10) $\frac{1}{216}$
11) $\frac{1}{256}$
12) $\frac{1}{900}$
13) $\frac{1}{17}$
14) $\frac{1}{196}$

15) $\frac{1}{361}$
16) $\frac{1}{18}$
17) $\frac{1}{6}$
18) $\frac{1}{15}$
19) $\frac{1}{21}$
20) $\frac{1}{81}$
21) $\frac{1}{64}$
22) $\frac{1}{20}$
23) $\frac{1}{144}$
24) $\frac{1}{128}$
25) $\frac{1}{13}$
26) $\frac{1}{35}$
27) $\frac{1}{27}$

28) $\frac{1}{729}$
29) $\frac{1}{10,000}$
30) $\frac{1}{729}$
31) 125
32) 64
33) $\frac{3}{2}$
34) $\frac{343}{27}$
35) 32
36) $\frac{9}{2}$
37) $\frac{11}{3}$
38) 36
39) $\frac{36}{25}$
40) 81
41) $\frac{100}{9}$
42) $\frac{9}{5}$

Division Property of Exponents

1) 9
2) $\frac{1}{5}$
3) 49
4) $\frac{1}{8}$
5) $\frac{2}{x}$
6) 1
7) 144
8) $\frac{1}{9}$

9) 4^3
10) $\frac{2}{3x}$
11) $\frac{5x}{7}$
12) $\frac{8x}{7}$
13) $\frac{15x}{11y^3}$
14) $\frac{3}{7xy}$
15) $\frac{4}{5}x^2$

16) $\frac{13y^5}{10}$
17) $\frac{9x}{8y^3}$
18) $\frac{15}{21x^2}$
19) $\frac{4}{5x}$
20) $\frac{21x}{25}$
21) $\frac{6x}{10}$

Powers of Products and Quotients

1) 6^{15}
2) 4^8
3) 3^9
4) 8^{15}
5) 6^{12}
6) 10^{15}
7) 3^{12}
8) 4^{15}
9) $64x^6$
10) $8x^9y^{15}$
11) $9x^4y^6$

12) $64x^{12}y^{15}$
13) $32x^{15}y^{20}$
14) $64x^9y^{12}$
15) $32x^{15}$
16) $125x^{21}$
17) $81x^{20}y^8$
18) $64x^{36}$
19) $36x^{14}y^2$
20) $49x^{18}y^{10}$
21) $216x^9y^{12}$
22) $256x^{16}y^{24}$

23) $1000x^3y^{15}$
24) $\frac{125}{x^6}$
25) x^2y^6
26) $\frac{4}{x^4}$
27) $\frac{8x^3}{y^9}$
28) $\frac{x^4}{y^{16}}$
29) $\frac{x^{10}}{9y^{10}}$
30) $\frac{10y}{x}$

Negative Exponents and Negative Bases

1) $-\frac{1}{81}$
2) $-\frac{1}{27}$
3) $-\frac{1}{5}$
4) $-\frac{1}{x^2}$
5) $\frac{1}{4x^2}$

6) $-\frac{3}{x^7}$
7) $-\frac{4}{x^2}$
8) $\frac{1}{25x^2y}$
9) $\frac{12}{x^3y^2}$
10) $\frac{11}{a^3b^2}$

11) $-\frac{6x^4}{y^5}$
12) $-20x^3$
13) $-15ba^3$
14) 16
15) -125
16) $-10a^2b^4$
17) $-7x^7$

18) $-\frac{b^4}{a^4}$

19) $-6x^4$

20) $-\frac{2bc^5}{3}$

21) $6a^5b^6$

22) $-\frac{3p^4}{4n^4}$

23) $-\frac{5ac^3}{4b^3}$

24) $-\frac{3c}{4a}$

25) $\frac{9y^2z^4}{x^4}$

26) $-\frac{5ac^6}{4b^3}$

27) $\frac{1}{4x^6}$

28) $9x^{12}$

29) $-\frac{1}{3x^2}$

Writing Scientific Notation

1) 2.11×10^{-1}
2) 5×10^{-3}
3) 8.5×10^{0}
4) 4.5×10^{1}
5) 9×10^{2}
6) 9×10^{-3}
7) 3.2×10^{1}
8) 3.2×10^{3}
9) 1.11×10^{4}
10) 7.1×10^{4}

11) 9×10^{7}
12) 8×10^{-7}
13) 5.41×10^{8}
14) 4.5×10^{-6}
15) 7.65×10^{-7}
16) 1.32×10^{8}
17) 4.9×10^{4}
18) 5.3×10^{7}
19) 3.56×10^{-6}
20) 1.9×10^{-8}

21) 0.007
22) 0.00006
23) 370,000
24) 0.00456
25) 0.00036
26) 420,000
27) 7,000,000
28) 2,100
29) 0.000000008
30) 0.000000756

Square Roots

1) 21
2) 23
3) 27
4) 13
5) 31
6) 17
7) 33
8) 45
9) 22
10) 12
11) 34
12) 28
13) 37

14) 0
15) 40
16) 41
17) 42
18) 50
19) $9\sqrt{5}$
20) $19\sqrt{6}$
21) $7\sqrt{3}$
22) $8\sqrt{7}$
23) 60
24) $10\sqrt{6}$
25) 9

26) 36
27) 42
28) 25
29) 56
30) 21
31) $3\sqrt{2}$
32) $7\sqrt{5}$
33) $2\sqrt{2}$
34) 150
35) 245
36) 0

Chapter 9:

Polynomials

Topics that you'll practice in this chapter:

✓ Writing Polynomials in Standard Form

✓ Simplifying Polynomials

✓ Adding and Subtracting Polynomials

✓ Multiplying Monomials

✓ Multiplying and Dividing Monomials

✓ Multiplying a Polynomial and a Monomial

✓ Multiplying Binomials

✓ Factoring Trinomials

✓ Operations with Polynomials

Writing Polynomials in Standard Form

✎ *Write each polynomial in standard form.*

1) $12x - 4x =$

2) $7 + 12x - 20x =$

3) $18x^2 - 9x^3 =$

4) $12 + 7x^3 - 5x =$

5) $8x^2 - x - 4x^4 =$

6) $-10x^5 + 3x - 2x^2 =$

7) $5x - 9x^2 - 4x^4 =$

8) $-5x^2 - 6x + 2x^3 =$

9) $6x^2 - 5 - x =$

10) $15x^2 - 13x - 15x^4 =$

11) $3x^2 - 8x + 7x^3 =$

12) $21 - 10x^2 + 4x^3 =$

13) $11x^3 - 2x + 7x^5 =$

14) $14x^4 - 9x^2 + 5x^6 =$

15) $-2x + 9x^2 - 7x^5 =$

16) $18x^4 + 6x^2 - 4x^3 + 1 =$

17) $11x^3 - 7x^5 - 16 + x^4 =$

18) $-3x^2 - 3x - 13x^3 - 2x =$

19) $14x^2 + 5x^3 - 2x^4 - 7x^2 =$

20) $7x^2 - 15x^4 - 6x^2 + 12x^4 =$

21) $14x^3 - x^4 + x^2 - 11x^3 =$

22) $2x^2 + 3x^4 + 7x^3 - 6x^2 =$

23) $2x(3x + 2 - 4x^2) =$

24) $8x(x^3 + 3x^2) =$

25) $4x(5x^3 - 7x - 2) =$

26) $2x(7 - 2x - 3x^4) =$

27) $x^2(2x^3 - 5x^4 + 1) =$

28) $7x(x^4 + 2x^2 - 4x) =$

29) $-2x(2x^3 - 3x^2 + 2x) =$

30) $3x^3(x - 2x^2 + x^4) =$

Simplifying Polynomials

✎ *Simplify each expression.*

1) $-4(3x - 2) =$

2) $3x(x + 3) =$

3) $-2x(8x - 5) =$

4) $6(-2x + 2) =$

5) $-6x(10x - 8) =$

6) $2x(8x + 1) =$

7) $(3x - 2)(x + 9) =$

8) $(x + 7)(4x + 5) =$

9) $(x - 2)(x - 7) =$

10) $(5x - 6)(2x - 3) =$

11) $(4x - 5)(2x + 4) =$

12) $7x^2 - 5x^2 + 6x^3 =$

13) $4x - 3x^2 - 2x^3 - 4x =$

14) $11x^3 + 4x^2 - 5x^3 =$

15) $17x^3 - 8x^4 - 15x^3 =$

16) $-12x^2 - 6x^3 - 11x^4 =$

17) $-3x^2 - 6x^3 + 14x^4 + 5x^3 =$

18) $3x - x^2 - 2x^4 - 5x^3 + 7x^4 =$

19) $5x^5 - x + 8x^3 + 3x - 8x^5 =$

20) $6 - 5x^2 - 3x^2 - 2x^3 - 6 =$

21) $5x^6 - 2x^2 + 5x^2 - 6x^6 =$

22) $(14x^4 - x) + (4x^3 - 7x^3) =$

23) $x(3x^2 - 6x^3 - x^4) =$

24) $-6(x^5 - 5) - 4(7 - x^2) =$

25) $8x^2 - x^3 + x + 1 - 9x^2 =$

26) $7 - 6x^2 + 8x^2 - x^3 + 7 =$

27) $(3x^2 - 5x) - (7x - 2 + 6x^2) =$

28) $4x^4 + 9x^3 - x^2(4x^2 + 5x) =$

29) $6x + 9x^4 - 3 - 2(x^4 + 1) =$

30) $5 - 8x^5 - x(3x^3 + x^2 - 4x^3) =$

31) $-5(x^6 + 1) - x(x + x^5) =$

32) $(2x^7 - x) - x^2(6x - 2x^5) =$

Adding and Subtracting Polynomials

✎ *Add or subtract expressions.*

1) $(2x^2 - 3) + (4x^2 + 5) =$

2) $(5x^2 - 2) - (2 + 6x^2) =$

3) $(6x^3 - 4x^2) - (3x^3 - 4) =$

4) $(4x^3 + 5x^2) - (3x^2 - 7x^3) =$

5) $(2x^4 - x) - (5x^4 + 5) =$

6) $(7x^2 - x^5) + (3x^5 - x^2) =$

7) $(6x^2 - 6) - (2 - 4x^2) =$

8) $(-x^5 - x^3) - (5x^3 + 2) =$

9) $(9x^2 - x^4) - (5x^2 + 5x^4) =$

10) $(9x + 5) - (4x + x) =$

11) $(6x^3 + x^4) - (9x^3 + x^4) =$

12) $(3x - 8x^7) - (3x^7 + 5x) =$

13) $(4x^2 - x^8) - (9x^8 + x^2) =$

14) $(6x^2 - x^7) + (x^2 - 3x^7) =$

15) $(6x^4 - 3x^2) - (x^4 - 6x^2) =$

16) $(-x^6 - 7x) + (8x + 4x^2) =$

17) $(9x + 2x^3) - (2x^3 + 8x) =$

18) $(3x - 7x^8) - (4x^8 - 5x^2) =$

19) $(4x^2 - x^5) + (3x^2 - 8x^5) =$

20) $(6x^2 + 2x^4) - (x^4 - x^2) =$

21) $(-12x^6 - 8x^2 + 15x^3) - (3x^3 - 8x^6 + 11x^2) =$

22) $(17x^5 - 8x^2 - 14x) - (-11x^2 - 20x^5 + 12x) =$

23) $(7x - 12x^2 - 4x^5) + (-5x^2 - 11x^5 - 8x) =$

24) $(4x^8 - x^5 + 3x) - (6x^5 + 8x^8 - 10x) =$

25) $(18x^7 - 2x^3 + x) - (-9x^3 + x^7 + 10x) =$

26) $(-13x^2 - 5x^4 + 8x^3) + (11x^3 - 9x^2 + 12x^4) =$

Multiplying Monomials

✏️ *Simplify each expression.*

1) $2u^3 \times (-3u^2) =$

2) $(-6p^2) \times (-2p^6) =$

3) $4x^2y^3z^2 \times 5z^3 =$

4) $6u^2t^5 \times (-4u^2t^4) =$

5) $(-5a^2) \times (2a^3b^3) =$

6) $-5a^2b^3 \times 6a^3b^2 =$

7) $5x^2y \times x^4y^2 =$

8) $4p^4q^2 \times (-6p^2q^4) =$

9) $6s^3t^5 \times 2s^3t^2 =$

10) $(-4x^2y^4) \times 2x^3y^3 =$

11) $10x^2y^3z \times 3z^5 =$

12) $7x^2y \times x^3y^6 =$

13) $5p^3q^2 \times (-4p^5q^4) =$

14) $11s^2t^6 \times 5st^2 =$

15) $8p^2 \times (-7p^3) =$

16) $(-2p^5q^2r^3) \times 3p^2q^3r^4 =$

17) $(-2a^2) \times 7a^3b^2) =$

18) $4u^2v^6 \times (-2u^6v^5) =$

19) $5u^5 \times (-6u^4) =$

20) $-3x^2y^3 \times 9x^2y^3 =$

21) $6y^3z^5 \times (-2\,y^6z^3) =$

22) $8a^6b^3c^4 \times 3a^2b^4c^3 =$

23) $(-3p^2q^2) \times (-2p^3q^5) =$

24) $5u^2v^4 \times (-6u^2v^6) =$

25) $14y^2z^3 \times (-4y^4z^3) =$

26) $(-3p^3qr^2) \times 4p^3qr^3 =$

27) $3a^3b^2c^3 \times (-3a^3bc^5) =$

28) $5x^2y^3z^6 \times 4x^3y^2z^3 =$

Multiplying and Dividing Monomials

✎ *Simplify each expression.*

1) $(5x^3)(x^4) =$

2) $(4x^2)(3x^3) =$

3) $(5x^3)(6x^7) =$

4) $(4x^2)(2x^4) =$

5) $(-11x^5)(4x^3) =$

6) $(5y^5x^6)(2y^4x^4) =$

7) $(4x^3y^2)(3x^3y^4) =$

8) $(-4x^2y^2)(2x^4y^3) =$

9) $(-4x^5y^7)(-5x^2y^6) =$

10) $(7x^2y^4)(-4x^5y^2) =$

11) $(12x^2y^4)(2x^9y^3) =$

12) $(5x^2y^5)(2x^2y^5) =$

13) $(9x^6y^2)(3x^4y^2) =$

14) $(5x^4y^2)(6x^4y^4) =$

15) $(6x^3y^4)(5x^2y^7) =$

16) $(-3x^2y^2)(4x^4y^6) =$

17) $\dfrac{12x^5y^4}{4x^5y^3} =$

18) $\dfrac{6x^3y^2}{2x^2y} =$

19) $\dfrac{10x^4y^5}{5x^2y^2} =$

20) $\dfrac{15x^5y^5}{5x^3y^4} =$

21) $\dfrac{16x^9y^3}{4x^8y^3} =$

22) $\dfrac{24x^5y^4}{8x^4y^4} =$

23) $\dfrac{35x^5y^4}{7x^2y^3} =$

24) $\dfrac{27x^{13}y^8}{9x^{10}y^6} =$

25) $\dfrac{42x^6y^{12}}{6x^6y^{10}} =$

26) $\dfrac{-36x^{11}y^8}{12x^3y^4} =$

27) $\dfrac{-81x^8y^{10}}{27x^7y^6} =$

Multiplying a Polynomial and a Monomial

✎ *Find each product.*

1) $2x(x - 5) =$

2) $-(3)(4 + 2x) =$

3) $8x(4x - 6) =$

4) $-2x(-3x + 1) =$

5) $8x(-4x - 8) =$

6) $7(5x - 2y) =$

7) $-3x(4x - y) =$

8) $5x(4x - 7y) =$

9) $-3x(4x + 7y) =$

10) $5x(3x - 8y) =$

11) $7x(7x - 12) =$

12) $3x(9x - 5y) =$

13) $8x(7x - 9y) =$

14) $-6x(7x - 2y - 3) =$

15) $6x(-x^3 - 3y^4) =$

16) $11x(3x - 2y^3) =$

17) $4(6x^3 - 10y^5) =$

18) $4x(-3x^3y^3 + 5y) =$

19) $-x(4x^5 + 4xy^3 + 6) =$

20) $5(2x^2 + 3x^2y - 5) =$

21) $6x(4x^3 + xy^2 - x) =$

22) $3x(-2x^3 + 4x + 3xy) =$

23) $x^2(2x^3 + 2xy - 2y^5) =$

24) $2x(3x^2 + 4x - 6) =$

25) $2(-5x^2 + 6x - 4) =$

26) $x^4(-2x^2 + 3y + 2) =$

27) $2x^3(5x^2 - 3y + x) =$

28) $15x^2(2x^3 + 3x - 4) =$

29) $5x^5(2x^4 + xy^5 - 3y^2) =$

30) $7x^4(2x^2 + 3x + 5y) =$

31) $4x^2(5x^2 - 2x + 1) =$

32) $6x(2x^4 + 4xy - y^5) =$

Multiplying Binomials

✎ *Find each product.*

1) $(x - 3)(x + 3) =$

2) $(x + 4)(x - 5) =$

3) $(x + 9)(x + 1) =$

4) $(x - 2)(x + 2) =$

5) $(x - 2)(x + 3) =$

6) $(x - 9)(x + 4) =$

7) $(x - 3)(x + 7) =$

8) $(x + 5)(x + 11) =$

9) $(x - 8)(x + 8) =$

10) $(x + 1)(x - 6) =$

11) $(x - 12)(x + 2) =$

12) $(x - 10)(x + 7) =$

13) $(x + 5)(x - 6) =$

14) $(x - 7)(x - 9) =$

15) $(x - 2)(x - 5) =$

16) $(x - 3)(x - 11) =$

17) $(x + 9)(x + 4) =$

18) $(x - 4)(x - 7) =$

19) $(3x + 1)(x - 2) =$

20) $(2x + 5)(x + 5) =$

21) $(x - 3)(4x - 5) =$

22) $(3x - 9)(2x - 1) =$

23) $(5x + 2)(x - 3) =$

24) $(4x + 3)(2x - 4) =$

25) $(2x + 1)(6x - 4) =$

26) $(7x + 2)(3x - 5) =$

27) $(2x - 3)(3x + 5) =$

28) $(7x - 4)(2x - 2) =$

29) $(5x - 4)(3x + 1) =$

30) $(2x + 6)(8x + 1) =$

31) $(4x + 6)(4x - 6) =$

32) $(2x^2 - 4)(x^2 + 8) =$

Factoring Trinomials

✎ *Factor each trinomial.*

1) $x^2 - 15x + 44 =$

2) $3x^2 + 23x - 8 =$

3) $x^2 - x - 56 =$

4) $2x^2 + x - 1 =$

5) $8x^2 - 39x - 5 =$

6) $x^2 - 8x - 9 =$

7) $x^2 - 4x - 32 =$

8) $x^2 - 8x - 84 =$

9) $x^2 - 81 =$

10) $x^2 + 20x + 96 =$

11) $4x^2 - 1 =$

12) $x^2 - x - 132 =$

13) $x^2 + 15x + 14 =$

14) $x^2 + 13x - 30 =$

15) $4x^2 + 8x - 32 =$

16) $7x^2 - 27x - 4 =$

17) $4x^2 + 16x - 48 =$

18) $2x^2 - 12x - 80 =$

19) $3x^2 + 19x - 14 =$

20) $12x^2 + 20x - 32 =$

✎ *Solve each problem.*

21) The area of a rectangle is $x^2 - 3x - 70$. If the width of rectangle is $x - 10$, what is its length? _____

22) The area of a parallelogram is $30x^2 + 4x - 48$ and its height is $5x - 6$. What is the base of the parallelogram? _____

23) The area of a rectangle is $9x^2 + 27x - 22$. If the width of the rectangle is $3x + 11$, what is its length? _____

Operations with Polynomials

✍ *Find each product.*

1) $-6(2x - 8) =$ _____

2) $5(4x + 11) =$ _____

3) $6(4x - 5) =$ _____

4) $-8(6x - 7) =$ _____

5) $5x^3(2x - x^2) =$ _____

6) $3x^2(9x - 8) =$ _____

7) $12x^2(9x^2 - 5x) =$ _____

8) $-12x^5(4x - x^3) =$ _____

9) $7(x^3 + 6x - 5) =$ _____

10) $10(2x^2 + 4x - 5) =$ _____

11) $6(2x^2 - 7x - 4) =$ _____

12) $5x(2x^2 + 8x + 2) =$ _____

13) $(8x + 6)(7x - 2) =$ _____

14) $(5x + 7)(2x - 1) =$ _____

15) $(4x - 9)(7x - 3) =$ _____

16) $(7x - 5)(2x^2 + 1) =$ _____

✍ *Solve each problem.*

17) The measures of two sides of a triangle are $(5x + 6y)$ and $(4x - 8y)$. If the perimeter of the triangle is $(18x + 3y)$, what is the measure of the third side? _____

18) The height of a triangle is $(6x - 2)$ and its base is $(8x + 1)$. What is the area of the triangle? _____

19) One side of a square is $(8x + 4)$. What is the area of the square? _____

20) The length of a rectangle is $(10x + y)$ and its width is $(9x - 3y)$. What is the perimeter of the rectangle? _____

21) The side of a cube measures $(x - 4)$. What is the volume of the cube? _____

22) If the perimeter of a rectangle is $(20x + 4y)$ and its width is $(3x + 2y)$, what is the length of the rectangle? _____

Answers

Writing Polynomials in Standard Form

1) $8x$
2) $-8x + 7$
3) $-9x^3 + 18x^2$
4) $7x^3 - 5x + 12$
5) $-4x^4 + 8x^2 - x$
6) $-10x^5 - 2x^2 + 3x$
7) $-4x^4 - 9x^2 + 5x$
8) $2x^3 - 5x^2 - 6x$
9) $6x^2 - x - 5$
10) $-15x^4 + 15x^2 - 13x$
11) $7x^3 + 3x^2 - 8x$
12) $4x^3 - 10x^2 + 21$
13) $7x^5 + 11x^3 - 2x$
14) $5x^6 + 14x^4 - 9x^2$
15) $-7x^5 + 9x^2 - 2x$
16) $18x^4 - 4x^3 + 6x^2 + 1$

17) $-7x^5 + x^4 + 11x^3 - 16$
18) $-13x^3 - 3x^2 - 5x$
19) $-2x^4 + 5x^3 + 7x^2$
20) $-3x^4 + x^2$
21) $-x^4 + 3x^3 + x^2$
22) $3x^4 + 7x^3 - 4x^2$
23) $-8x^3 + 6x^2 + 4x$
24) $8x^4 + 24x^3$
25) $20x^4 - 28x^2 - 8x$
26) $-6x^5 - 4x^2 + 14x$
27) $-5x^6 + 2x^5 + x^2$
28) $7x^5 + 14x^3 - 28x^2$
29) $-4x^4 + 6x^3 - 4x^2$
30) $3x^7 - 6x^5 + 3x^4$

Simplifying Polynomials

1) $-12x + 8$
2) $3x^2 + 9x$
3) $-16x^2 + 10x$
4) $-12x^2 + 12$
5) $-60x^2 + 48x$
6) $16x^2 + 2x$
7) $3x^2 + 25x - 18$
8) $4x^2 + 33x + 35$
9) $x^2 - 9x + 14$
10) $10x^2 - 27x + 18$
11) $8x^2 + 6x - 20$
12) $6x^3 + 2x^2$
13) $-2x^3 - 3x^2$
14) $6x^3 + 4x^2$
15) $-8x^4 + 2x^3$
16) $-11x^4 - 6x^3 - 12x^2$
17) $14x^4 - x^3 - 3x^2$

18) $5x^4 - 5x^3 - x^2 + 3x$
19) $-3x^5 + 8x^3 + 2x$
20) $-2x^3 - 8x^2$
21) $-x^6 + 3x^2$
22) $14x^4 - 3x^3 - x$
23) $-x^5 - 6x^4 + 3x^3$
24) $-6x^5 + 4x^2 + 2$
25) $-x^3 - x^2 + x + 1$
26) $-x^3 + 2x^2$
27) $-3x^2 - 12x + 2$
28) $4x^3$
29) $7x^4 + 6x - 5$
30) $-8x^5 + x^4 - x^3 + 5$
31) $-6x^6 - x^2 - 5$
32) $4x^7 - 6x^3 - x$

Adding and Subtracting Polynomials

1) $6x^2 + 2$
2) $-x^2 - 4$
3) $3x^3 - 4x^2 + 4$
4) $11x^3 + 2x^2$
5) $-3x^4 - x - 5$
6) $2x^5 + 6x^2$
7) $10x^2 - 8$
8) $-x^5 - 6x^3 - 2$
9) $-6x^4 + 4x^2$
10) $4x + 5$
11) $-3x^3$
12) $-11x^7 - 2x$
13) $-10x^8 + 3x^2$

14) $-4x^7 + 7x^2$
15) $5x^4 + 3x^2$
16) $-x^6 + 4x^2 + x$
17) x
18) $-11x^8 + 5x^2 + 3x$
19) $-9x^5 + 7x^2$
20) $x^4 + 7x^2$
21) $-4x^6 + 12x^3 - 19x^2$
22) $37x^5 + 3x^2 - 26x$
23) $-15x^5 - 17x^2 - x$
24) $-4x^8 - 7x^5 + 13x$
25) $17x^7 + 7x^3 - 9x$
26) $7x^4 + 19x^3 - 22x^2$

Multiplying Monomials

1) $-6u^5$
2) $12p^8$
3) $20x^2y^3z^5$
4) $-24u^4t^9$
5) $-10a^5b^3$
6) $-30a^5b^5$
7) $5x^6y^3$
8) $-24p^6q^6$
9) $12s^6t^7$
10) $-8x^5y^7$
11) $30x^2y^3z^6$

12) $7x^5y^7$
13) $-20p^8q^6$
14) $55s^3t^8$
15) $-56p^5$
16) $-6p^7q^5r^7$
17) $-14a^5b^2$
18) $-8u^8v^{11}$
19) $-30u^9$

20) $-27x^4y^6$
21) $-12y^9z^8$
22) $24a^8b^7c^7$
23) $6p^5q^7$
24) $-30u^4v^{10}$
25) $-56y^6z^6$
26) $-12p^6q^2r^5$
27) $-9a^6b^3c^8$
28) $20x^5y^5z^9$

Multiplying and Dividing Monomials

1) $5x^7$
2) $12x^5$
3) $30x^{10}$
4) $8x^6$
5) $-44x^8$
6) $10x^{10}y^9$
7) $12x^6y^6$
8) $-8x^6y^5$

9) $20x^7y^{13}$
10) $-28x^7y^6$
11) $24x^{11}y^7$
12) $10x^4y^{10}$
13) $27x^{10}y^4$
14) $30x^8y^6$
15) $30x^5y^{11}$
16) $-12x^6y^8$

17) $3y$
18) $3xy$
19) $2x^2y^3$
20) $3x^2y$
21) $4x$
22) $3x$
23) $5x^3y$
24) $3x^3y^2$

25) $7y^2$ 26) $-3x^8y^4$ 27) $-3xy^4$

Multiplying a Polynomial and a Monomial

1) $2x^2 - 10x$
2) $-6x - 12$
3) $32x^2 - 48x$
4) $6x^2 - 2x$
5) $-32x^2 - 64x$
6) $35x - 14y$
7) $-12x^2 + 3xy$
8) $20x^2 - 35xy$
9) $-12x^2 - 21xy$
10) $15x^2 - 40xy$
11) $49x^2 - 84x$
12) $27x^2 - 15xy$
13) $56x^2 - 72xy$
14) $-42x^2 + 12xy + 18x$
15) $-6x^4 - 18xy^4$
16) $33x^2 - 22xy^3$
17) $24x^3 - 40y^5$

18) $-12x^4y^3 + 20xy$
19) $-4x^6 - 4x^2y^3 - 6x$
20) $10x^2 + 15x^2y - 25$
21) $24x^4 + 6x^2y^2 - 6x^2$
22) $-6x^4 + 12x^2 + 9x^2y$
23) $2x^5 + 2x^3y - 2x^2y^5$
24) $6x^3 + 8x^2 - 12x$
25) $-10x^2 + 12x - 8$
26) $-2x^6 + 3x^4y + 2x^4$
27) $10x^5 - 6x^3y + 2x^4$
28) $30x^5 + 45x^3 - 60x^2$
29) $10x^9 + 5x^6y^5 - 15x^5y^2$
30) $14x^6 + 21x^5 + 35x^4y$
31) $20x^4 - 8x^3 + 4x^2$
32) $12x^5 + 24x^2y - 6xy^5$

Multiplying Binomials

1) $x^2 - 9$
2) $x^2 - x - 20$
3) $x^2 + 10x + 9$
4) $x^2 - 4$
5) $x^2 + x - 6$
6) $x^2 - 5x - 36$
7) $x^2 + 4x - 21$
8) $x^2 + 16x + 55$
9) $x^2 - 64$
10) $x^2 - 5x - 6$
11) $x^2 - 10x - 24$
12) $x^2 - 3x - 70$
13) $x^2 - x - 30$
14) $x^2 - 16x + 63$
15) $x^2 - 7x + 10$
16) $x^2 - 14x + 33$

17) $x^2 + 13x + 36$
18) $x^2 - 11x + 28$
19) $3x^2 - 5x - 2$
20) $2x^2 + 15x + 25$
21) $4x^2 - 17x + 15$
22) $6x^2 - 21x + 9$
23) $5x^2 - 13x - 6$
24) $8x^2 - 10x - 12$
25) $12x^2 - 2x - 4$
26) $21x^2 - 29x - 10$
27) $6x^2 + x - 15$
28) $14x^2 - 22x + 8$
29) $15x^2 - 7x - 4$
30) $16x^2 + 50x + 6$
31) $16x^2 - 36$
32) $2x^4 + 12x^2 - 32$

Factoring Trinomials

1) $(x-4)(x-11)$

2) $(3x-1)(x+8)$

3) $(x-8)(x+7)$

4) $(2x-1)(x+1)$

5) $(8x+1)(x-5)$

6) $(x+1)(x-9)$

7) $(x+4)(x-8)$

8) $(x+6)(x-14)$

9) $(x+9)(x-9)$

10) $(x+8)(x+12)$

11) $(2x+1)(2x-1)$

12) $(x-12)(x+11)$

13) $(x+14)(x+1)$

14) $(x+15)(x-2)$

15) $(2x+8)(2x-4)$

16) $(7x+1)(x-4)$

17) $(4x-8)(x+6)$

18) $(x-10)(2x+8)$

19) $(3x-2)(x+7)$

20) $(4x-4)(3x+8)$

21) $(x+7)$

22) $(6x+8)$

23) $(3x-2)$

Operations with Polynomials

1) $-12x+48$

2) $20x+55$

3) $24x-30$

4) $-48x+56$

5) $10x^4-5x^5$

6) $27x^3-24x^2$

7) $108x^4-60x^3$

8) $-48x^6+12x^8$

9) $7x^3+42x-35$

10) $20x^2+40x-50$

11) $12x^2-42x-24$

12) $10x^3+40x^2+10x$

13) $56x^2-26x-12$

14) $10x^2+9x-7$

15) $28x^2-75x+27$

16) $14x^3-10x^2+7x-5$

17) $(9x+5y)$

18) $24x^2-5x-1$

19) $64x^2+64x+16$

20) $38x-4y$

21) $x^3-12x^2+48x-64$

22) $7x$

Chapter 10:

Geometry and Solid Figures

Topics that you'll practice in this chapter:

✓ Angles

✓ Pythagorean Relationship

✓ Triangles

✓ Polygons

✓ Trapezoids

✓ Circles

✓ Cubes

✓ Rectangular Prism

✓ Cylinder

✓ Pyramids and Cone

Angles

✎ **What is the value of x in the following figures?**

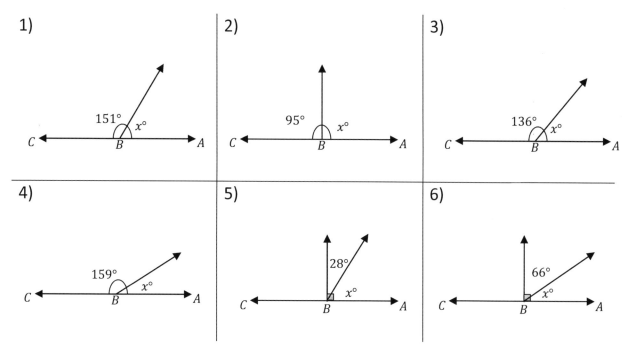

1) 151° $x°$

2) 95° $x°$

3) 136° $x°$

4) 159° $x°$

5) 28° $x°$

6) 66° $x°$

✎ *Solve.*

7) Two complementary angles have equal measures. What is the twice measure of each angle? _____

8) The measure of an angle is four fifth the measure of its supplement. What is the measure of the angle? _____

9) Two angles are complementary and the measure of one angle is 36 less than the other. What is the measure of the bigger angle? _____

10) Two angles are complementary. The measure of one angle is five times the measure of the other. What is the measure of the smaller angle? _____

11) Two supplementary angles are given. The measure of one angle is 66° less than the measure of the other. What does the bigger angle measure? _____

Pythagorean Relationship

✎ *Do the following lengths form a right triangle?*

1)
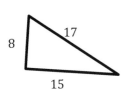

2)
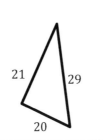

3)
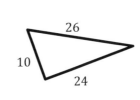

4)
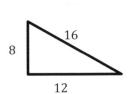

5)

6)
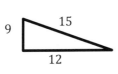

7)
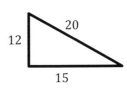

8)
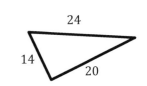

✎ *Find the missing side?*

9)
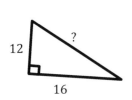

10)
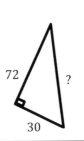

11)
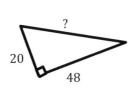

12)
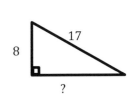

13)

14)
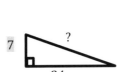

15)
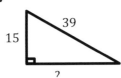

16)
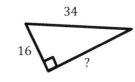

Triangles

✍ *Find the measure of the unknown angle in each triangle.*

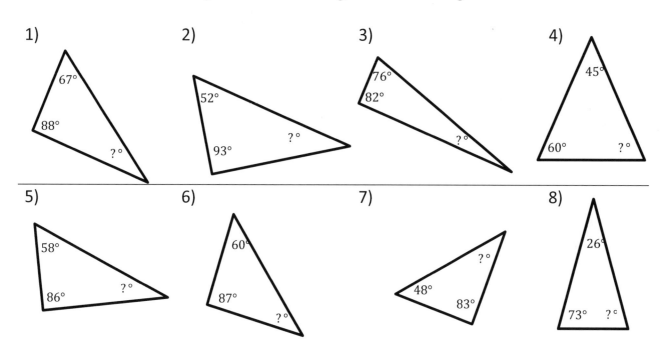

1) 67° 88° ?°

2) 52° 93° ?°

3) 76° 82° ?°

4) 45° 60° ?°

5) 58° 86° ?°

6) 60° 87° ?°

7) ?° 48° 83°

8) 26° 73° ?°

✍ *Find area of each triangle.*

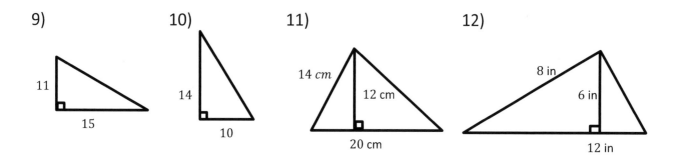

9) 11 15

10) 14 10

11) 14 cm 12 cm 20 cm

12) 8 in 6 in 12 in

Polygons

✍ **Find the perimeter of each shape.**

1)

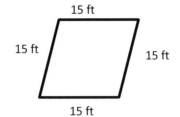

15 ft
15 ft   15 ft
15 ft

2)

16 in
13 in   13 in
16 in

3)

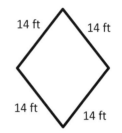

14 ft   14 ft
14 ft   14 ft

4) Square

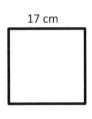

17 cm

5) Regular hexagon

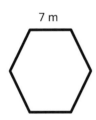

7 m

6)

8.2 cm
6.7 cm
5.3
6.7 cm
8.2 cm

7) Parallelogram

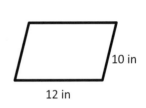

10 in
12 in

8) Square

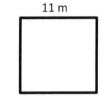

11 m

✍ **Find the area of each shape.**

9) Parallelogram

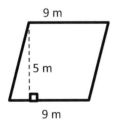

9 m
5 m
9 m

10) Rectangle

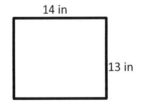

14 in
13 in

11) Rectangle

12 km
6 km

12) Square

9 in

112

Trapezoids

✎ *Find the area of each trapezoid.*

1)

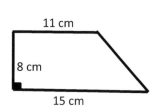

2)

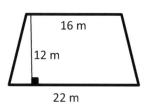

3)

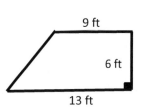

4)

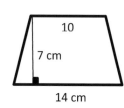

5)

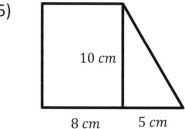

6)

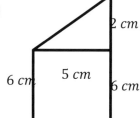

7)

8)

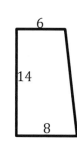

✎ *Solve.*

9) A trapezoid has an area of 96 cm² and its height is 6 cm and one base is 18 cm. What is the other base length? _____

10) If a trapezoid has an area of 204 ft² and the lengths of the bases are 19 ft and 15 ft, find the height. _____

11) If a trapezoid has an area of 340 m² and its height is 17 m and one base is 22 m, find the other base length. _____

12) The area of a trapezoid is 528 ft² and its height is 32 ft. If one base of the trapezoid is 14 ft, what is the other base length? _____

Circles

✎ **Find the area of each circle.** ($\pi = 3.14$)

1)　　　 2)　　　 3)　　　 4)　　　 5)　　　 6)

  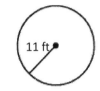

7)　　　 8)　　　 9)　　　 10)　　　 11)　　　 12)

     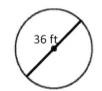

✎ **Complete the table below.** ($\pi = 3.14$)

	Radius	Diameter	Circumference	Area
Circle 1	5 inches	10 inches	31.4 inches	78.5 square inches
Circle 2		18 meters		
Circle 3				153.86 square ft
Circle 4			12.56 miles	
Circle 5		7 kilometers		
Circle 6	10 centimeters			
Circle 7		22 feet		
Circle 8				63.585 square meters
Circle 9			75.36 inches	
Circle 10	1.5 feet			

114

Cubes

✏️ *Find the volume of each cube.*

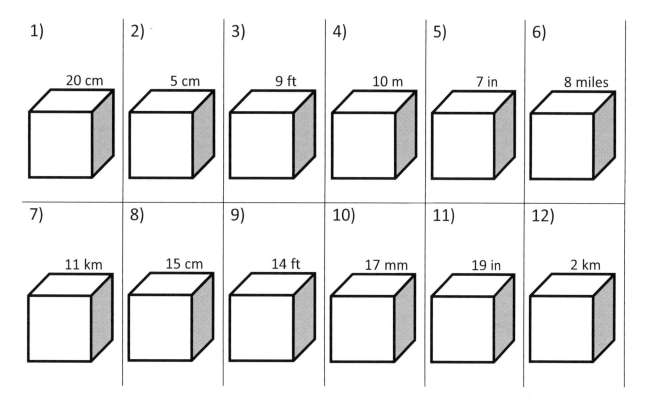

1) 20 cm
2) 5 cm
3) 9 ft
4) 10 m
5) 7 in
6) 8 miles
7) 11 km
8) 15 cm
9) 14 ft
10) 17 mm
11) 19 in
12) 2 km

✏️ *Find the surface area of each cube.*

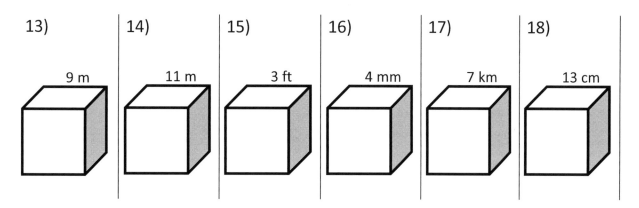

13) 9 m
14) 11 m
15) 3 ft
16) 4 mm
17) 7 km
18) 13 cm

Rectangular Prism

✍ **Find the volume of each Rectangular Prism.**

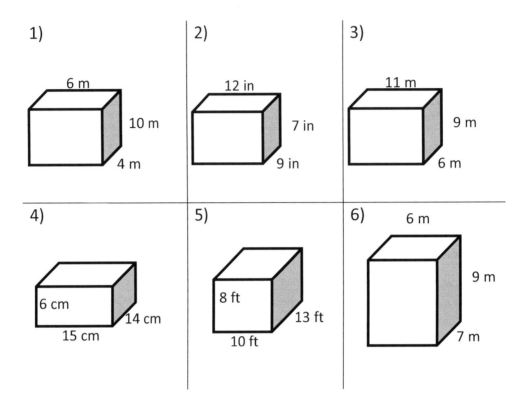

1)
6 m
10 m
4 m

2)
12 in
7 in
9 in

3)
11 m
9 m
6 m

4)
6 cm
15 cm
14 cm

5)
8 ft
13 ft
10 ft

6)
6 m
9 m
7 m

✍ **Find the surface area of each Rectangular Prism.**

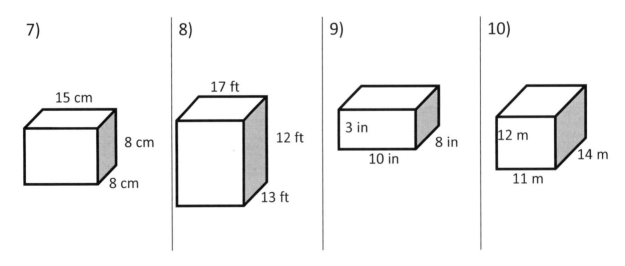

7)
15 cm
8 cm
8 cm

8)
17 ft
12 ft
13 ft

9)
3 in
10 in
8 in

10)
12 m
11 m
14 m

Cylinder

✏️ **Find the volume of each Cylinder. Round your answer to the nearest tenth.** ($\pi = 3.14$)

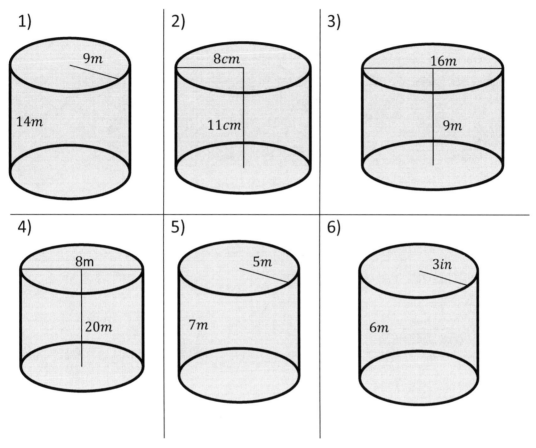

1) 9m, 14m	2) 8cm, 11cm	3) 16m, 9m
4) 8m, 20m	5) 5m, 7m	6) 3in, 6m

✏️ **Find the surface area of each Cylinder.** ($\pi = 3.14$)

7) 9m, 6m

8) 10m, 10m

9) 3m, 13m

10) 5m, 4m

Pyramids and Cone

✍️ *Find the volume of each Pyramid and Cone.* (π = 3.14)

1)

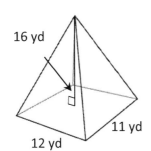

16 yd
11 yd
12 yd

2)

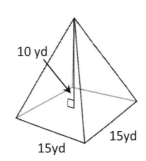

10 yd
15yd
15yd

3)

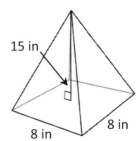

15 in
8 in
8 in

4)

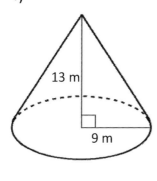

13 m
9 m

5)

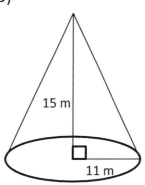

15 m
11 m

6)

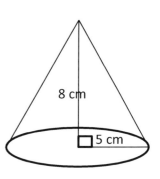

8 cm
5 cm

✍️ *Find the surface area of each Pyramid and Cone.* (π = 3.14)

7)

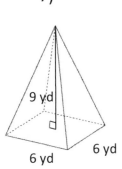

9 yd
6 yd
6 yd

8)

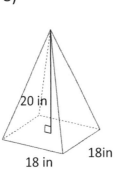

20 in
18 in
18in

9)

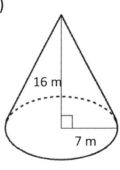

16 m
7 m

10)

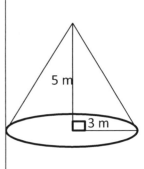

5 m
3 m

Answers

Angles

1) 29°
2) 85°
3) 44°
4) 21°

5) 62°
6) 24°
7) 90°
8) 144°

9) 63°
10) 15°
11) 123°

Pythagorean Relationship

1) Yes
2) Yes
3) Yes
4) NO
5) Yes
6) Yes

7) NO
8) NO
9) 20
10) 78
11) 52
12) 15

13) 12
14) 25
15) 36
16) 30

Triangles

1) 25°
2) 35°
3) 22°
4) 75°

5) 36°
6) 33°
7) 49°
8) 81°

9) 82.5 *square unites*
10) 70 *square unites*
11) 120 *square unites*
12) 36 *square unites*

Polygons

1) 60 *ft*
2) 58 *in*
3) 56 *ft*
4) 68 *cm*
5) 42 *m*

6) 29.8 *cm*
7) 44 *in*
8) 44 *m*
9) 45 m^2

10) 182 in^2
11) 72 km^2
12) 81 in^2

Trapezoids

1) 104 cm^2
2) 228 m^2
3) 66 ft^2
4) 84 cm^2

5) 105 cm^2
6) 35cm^2
7) 250
8) 98

9) 14 *cm*
10) 12 *ft*
11) 18 *m*
12) 19 *ft*

Circles

1) 153.86 in^2
2) 452.16 cm^2
3) 379.94 ft^2

4) 706.5 m^2
5) 907.46 cm^2
6) 1384.74 $miles^2$

7) 314 in^2
8) 254.34 ft^2
9) 200.96 m^2

10) $615.44\ cm^2$ 11) $379.94\ miles^2$ 12) $1017.36\ ft^2$

	Radius	Diameter	Circumference	Area
Circle 1	5 inches	10 inches	31.4 inches	78.5 square inches
Circle 2	9 meters	18 meters	56.52 meters	254.34 meters
Circle 3	7 square ft	14 square ft	43.93 square ft	153.86 square ft
Circle 4	2 miles	4 miles	12.56 miles	12.56 miles
Circle 5	3.5 kilometers	7 kilometers	21.98 kilometers	38.465 kilometers
Circle 6	10 centimeters	20 centimeters	62.8 centimeters	314 centimeters
Circle 7	11 feet	22 feet	69.08 feet	379.94 feet
Circle 8	4.5 square meters	9 square meters	28.26 square meters	63.585 square meters
Circle 9	12 inches	24 inches	75.36 inches	452.16 inches
Circle 10	1.5 feet	3 feet	9.42 feet	7.065 feet

Cubes

1) $8,000cm^3$
2) $125\ cm^3$
3) $729\ ft^3$
4) $1,000\ m^3$
5) $343\ in^3$
6) $512\ miles^3$

7) $1,331\ km^3$
8) $3,375\ cm^3$
9) $2,744\ ft^3$
10) $4,913\ mm^3$
11) $6,859\ in^3$
12) $8\ km^3$

13) $486m^2$
14) $726\ m^2$
15) $54\ ft^2$
16) $96\ mm^2$
17) $294\ km^2$
18) $1014\ cm^2$

Rectangular Prism

1) $240\ m^3$
2) $756\ in^3$
3) $594\ m^3$
4) $1,260\ cm^3$

5) $1,040\ ft^3$
6) $378\ m^3$
7) $608\ cm^2$
8) $1,162\ ft^2$

9) $268\ in2$
10) $908\ m^2$

Cylinder

1) $3,560.76\ m^3$
2) $2,210.56\ cm^3$
3) $1,808.64\ cm^3$
4) $1,004.8\ m^3$

5) $549.5\ m^3$
6) $169.56\ in^3$
7) $847.8\ m^2$
8) $1256\ cm^2$

9) $301.44\ cm^2$
10) $282.6\ m^2$

Pyramids and Cone

1) $704\ yd^3$
2) $750\ yd^3$
3) $320\ in^3$
4) $1,102.14\ m^3$

5) $1,899.7\ m^3$
6) $209.33cm^3$
7) $144\ yd^2$
8) $1,044\ in^2$

9) $505.54\ m^2$
10) $75.36\ m^2$

Chapter 11:

Statistics and Probability

Topics that you'll practice in this chapter:

✓ Mean and Median

✓ Mode and Range

✓ Histograms

✓ Stem–and–Leaf Plot

✓ Pie Graph

✓ Probability Problems

Mean and Median

✍ *Find Mean and Median of the Given Data.*

1) 5, 7, 9, 12, 12, 14, 16, 20

2) 30,21,15,12,10,6,16,4,12

3) 5,7,11,19,25,17,17,15

4) 6,10,8,12,6,14,18,22

5) 40,25,15,20,25,30,20

6) 24,12,10,12,16,18,20

7) 6,4,8,10,6,5,5,4,6

8) 60,20,25,30,45,60

9) 25,16,12,16,14,18,18

10) 44,42,52,68,70

11) 82,56,96,100,76

12) 76,68,24,30,30,60

✍ *Solve.*

13) In a javelin throw competition, five athletics score 45, 50, 66, 54 and 52 meters. What are their Mean and Median? _____

14) Eva went to shop and bought 6 apples, 4 peaches, 5 bananas, 3 pineapple and 2 melons. What are the Mean and Median of her purchase?

_____

15) Bob has 12 black pen, 16 red pen, 14 green pens, 20 blue pens and 2 boxes of yellow pens. If the Mean and Median are 14 and 14 respectively, what is the number of yellow pens in each box? _____

Mode and Range

✍ *Find Mode and Rage of the Given Data.*

1) 2,9,7,4,6,12,4

Mode: _____   Range: _____

2) 12,14,16,18,22,10,12

Mode: _____   Range: _____

3) 8,4,9,7,9,12,10,12,14,6,4

Mode: _____   Range: _____

4) 5,1,3,5,4,9,6,2,8,7

Mode: _____   Range: _____

5) 10,16,14,10,13,15

Mode: _____   Range: _____

6) 2,8,17,10,15,19,20,17,13

Mode: _____   Range: _____

7) 2,6,5,8,19,35,14,6

Mode: _____   Range: _____

8) 16,5,10,50,42,41,50

Mode: _____   Range: _____

9) 12,25,96,21,14,16,12

Mode: _____   Range: _____

10) 6,5,9,9,12,14,18,13

Mode: _____   Range: _____

11) 20,21,25,62,41,15,21

Mode: _____   Range: _____

12) 11,12,18,18,17,16,15,19

Mode: _____   Range: _____

✍ *Solve.*

13) A stationery sold 14 pencils, 21 red pens, 36 blue pens, 15 notebooks, 14 erasers, 28 rulers and 30 color pencils. What are the Mode and Range for the stationery sells?

Mode: _____   Range: _____

14) In an English test, eight students score 13,15,16,17,16,15,19and 15. What are their Mode and Range? _____

15) What is the range of the Prime numbers less than 25? _____

Histograms

✍ *Use the following Graph to complete the table.*

Day	Distance (km)
1	
2	

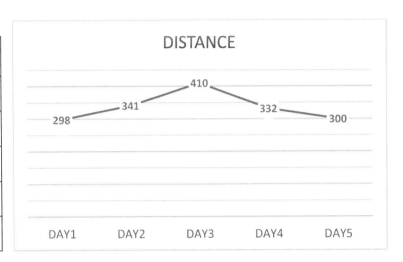

The following table shows the number of births in the US from 2007 to 2012 (in millions).

Year	Number of births (in millions)
2007	3.45
2008	3.98
2009	5.1
2010	4.85
2011	4.62
2012	4.25

Draw a histogram for the table.

Stem–and–Leaf Plot

Example:

56, 58, 42, 48, 66, 64, 53, 69, 45, 72

Stem	leaf		
4	2	5	8
5	3	6	8
6	4	6	9
7	2		

✏ *Make stem and leaf plots for the given data.*

1) 65,49,75,68,42,69,72,43,77

        Stem | Leaf plot

2) 24,51,44,29,34,59,47,55,21,38

        Stem | Leaf plot

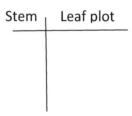

        Stem | Leaf plot

3) 72,69,84,92,98,74,63,88,66,94,79,91

Pie Graph

The circle graph below shows all Jason's expenses for last month. Jason spent $1,200 on his bills last month.

Answer following questions based on the Pie graph.

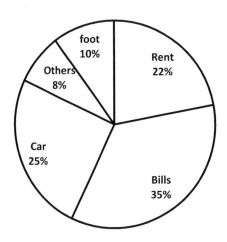

1- How much did Jason spend on his car last month? _____

2- How much did Jason spend for foods last month? _____

3- How much did Jason spend on his rent last month? _____

4- What fraction is Jason's expenses for his bills and Car out of his total

   expenses last month? _____

5- How much was Jason's total expenses last month? _____

Probability Problems

✍ *Solve.*

1) A number is chosen at random from 1 to 15. Find the probability of selecting number 7 or smaller numbers. _____

2) Bag A contains 10 red marbles and 5 green marbles. Bag B contains 16 black marbles and 8 orange marbles. What is the probability of selecting a green marble at random from bag A? What is the probability of selecting a black marble at random from Bag B? _____ _____

3) A number is chosen at random from 1 to 30. What is the probability of selecting multiples of 4. _____

4) A card is chosen from a well-shuffled deck of 52 cards. What is the probability that the card will be a 10 or 9 number card? _____

5) A number is chosen at random from 1 to 20. What is the probability of selecting a multiple of 5. _____

A spinner, numbered 1–12, is spun once. What is the probability of spinning …

6) an EVEN number? _____   7) a multiple of 2? _____

8) a PRIME number? _____   9) number 9? _____

Combinations and Permutations

✎ **Calculate the value of each.**

1) 6! = ____

2) 2! × 4! = ____

3) 3! = ____

4) 5! + 4! = ____

5) 10! = ____

6) 7! − 3! = ____

7) 5! + 7! = ____

8) 6! − 2! = ____

✎ **Solve each word problems.**

9) Susan is baking cookies. She uses sugar, flour, butter, cream and eggs. How many different orders of ingredients can she try? _____

10) Jason is planning for his vacation. He wants to go to museum, watch a movie, go to the beach, and play volleyball and soccer. How many different ways of ordering are there for him? _____

11) How many 8-digit numbers can be named using the digits 1, 2, 3, 4, 5, and 6 without repetition? _____

12) In how many ways can 4 boys be arranged in a straight line? _____

13) In how many ways can 7 athletes be arranged in a straight line? _____

14) A professor is going to arrange her 8 students in a straight line. In how many ways can she do this? _____

15) How many code symbols can be formed with the letters for the word YELLOW? _____

16) In how many ways a team of 7 basketball players can to choose a captain and co-captain? _____

Answers

Mean and Median

1) Mean: 11.875, Median: 12
2) Mean: 14, Median: 12
3) Mean: 14.5, Median: 16
4) Mean: 12, Median: 11
5) Mean: 25, Median: 25

6) Mean: 16, , Median: 16
7) Mean: 6, Median: 6
8) Mean: 40, Median: 37.5
9) Mean: 17, Median: 16
10) Mean: 55.2, Median: 52

11) Mean: 82, Median: 82
12) Mean: 48, Median: 45
13) Mean: 53.4, Median: 52
14) Mean: 4, Median: 4
15) 4

Mode and Range

1) Mode: 4, Range: 10
2) Mode: 12, Range: 12
3) Mode: 4,9,12, Range: 10
4) Mode: 5, Range: 8
5) Mode: 10, Range: 6

6) Mode: 17, Range: 18
7) Mode: 6, Range: 33
8) Mode: 50, Range: 45
9) Mode: 12, Range: 84
10) Mode: 9, Range: 13

11) Mode: 21, Range: 47
12) Mode: 18, Range: 8
13) Mode: 14, Range: 22
14) Mode: 15, Range: 6
15) 22

Histograms

Day	Distance (km)
1	298
2	341
3	410
4	332
5	300

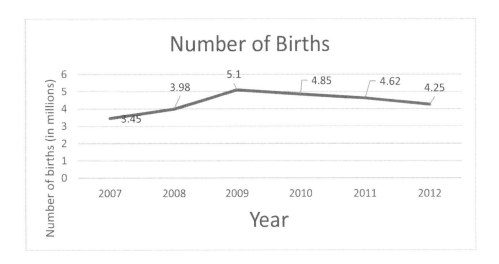

Stem–And–Leaf Plot

1)

Stem	leaf
4	2 3 9
6	5 8 9
7	2 5 7

2)

Stem	Leaf
2	1 4 9
3	4 8
4	4 7
5	1 5 9

3)

Stem	leaf
6	3 6 9
7	2 4 9
8	4 8
9	1 2 4 8

Pie Graph

1) $300
2) $120
3) $264
4) $\frac{6}{10}$
5) $1,200

Probability Problems

1) $\frac{7}{15}$

2) $\frac{1}{3}, \frac{2}{3}$

3) $\frac{7}{30}$

4) $\frac{2}{13}$

5) $\frac{1}{5}$

6) $\frac{1}{2}$

7) $\frac{1}{2}$

8) $\frac{5}{12}$

9) $\frac{1}{12}$

Combinations and Permutations

1) 720
2) 48
3) 6
4) 144
5) 3,628,800
6) 5,034
7) 5,160
8) 718
9) 120
10) 120
11) 720
12) 24
13) 5,040
14) 40,320
15) 720
16) 42

MCAS Mathematics Practice Tests

Time to Test

Time to refine your skill with a practice examination

Take these practice Grade 8 MCAS Math Tests to simulate the test day experience. After you've finished, score your test using the answer key.

Before You Start

- You'll need a pencil and calculator to take the test.

- For these practice tests, don't time yourself. Spend time as much as you need.

- It's okay to guess. You won't lose any points if you're wrong.

- After you've finished the test, review the answer key to see where you went wrong.

Graphing calculators are permitted for Grade 8 MCAS Tests

Good Luck!

MCAS Math Practice Test 1

Grade 8

Mathematics

2019

1) A pizza cut into 8 slices. Jason and his sister Eva ordered two pizzas. Jason ate $\frac{1}{2}$ of his pizza and Eva ate $\frac{3}{4}$ of her pizza. What part of the two pizzas was left?

A. $\frac{1}{2}$ C. $\frac{3}{8}$

B. $\frac{1}{3}$ D. $\frac{5}{8}$

2) Robert is preparing to run a marathon. He runs $3\frac{1}{10}$ miles on Saturday and two times that many on Monday and Wednesday. Robert wants to run a total of 18 miles this week. How many more miles does he need to run? Write your answer in the box below.

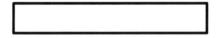

3) 20 more than twice a positive integer is 68 What is the integer?

A. 24   C. 26

B. 28   D. 30

4) $[3 \times (-21) + (5 \times 2)] - (-25) + [(-3) \times 6] \div 2 =?$

Write your answer in the box below.

5) A girl 160cm tall, stands 380cm from a lamp post at night. Her shadow from the light is 100cm long. How high is the lamp post?

Write your answer in the box below.

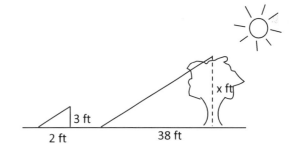

160 cm

100 cm   380 cm

6) If a tree casts a 38ft shadow at the same time that a yardstick casts a 2ft shadow, what is the height of the tree?

A. 24ft.

B. 27ft.

C. 57ft.

D. 48ft.

3 ft

2 ft   38 ft   x ft

7) Mike is 7.5 miles ahead of Julia running at 5.5 miles per hour and Julia is running at the speed of 8 miles per hour. How long does it take Julia to catch Mike?

A. 2 hours   C. 7.5 hours

B. 5.5 hours   D. 3 hours

8) A company pays its employer $7,000 plus 2% of all sales profit. If x is the number of all sales profit, which of the following represents the employer's revenue?

A. $0.02x$ C. $0.02x + 7,000$

B. $0.98x - 7,000$ D. $0.98x + 7,000$

9) Jason needs an 75% average in his writing class to pass. On his first 4 exams, he earned scores of 68%, 72%, 85%, and 90%. What is the minimum score Jason can earn on his fifth and final test to pass?

Write your answer in the box below.

```
┌──────────────────────────┐
│                          │
│                          │
└──────────────────────────┘
```

10) If 25% of a number is 8, what is the number?

A. 30   C. 32

B. 34   D. 36

11) An angle is equal to one fifth of its supplement. What is the measure of that angle?

A. 20   C. 45

B. 30   D. 60

12) Which graph shows linear equation $y = x + 1$?

A.

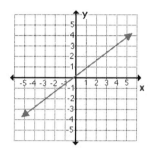

B.

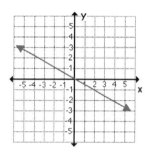

C.

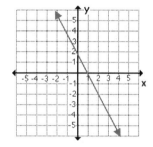

D.

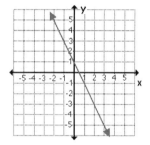

13) What is the solution of the following system of equations?

$$\begin{cases} \dfrac{-x}{2} + \dfrac{y}{4} = 1 \\ \dfrac{-5y}{6} + 2x = 4 \end{cases}$$

   A. $x = 48, y = 22$ C. $x = 20, y = 50$

   B. $x = 50, y = 20$ D. $x = 22, y = 48$

14) Which of the following values for x and y satisfy the following system of equations?

$$\begin{cases} x + 4y = 10 \\ 5x + 10y = 20 \end{cases}$$

A. $x = 3, y = 2$ C. $x = -2, y = 3$

B. $x = 2, y - 3$ D. $x = 3, y = -2$

15) The average of 21, 18, 16 and x is 20. What is the value of x?

A. 23   C. 30

B. 25   D. 20

16)   Which of the equation represents the compound inequality?

$$5 \leq 3x - 1 < 11$$

A. $3 \leq x < 5$ C. $2 \leq x < 6$

B. $2 \leq x < 4$ D. $1 \leq x < 4$

17) Point A $(-2, 6)$ and point B $(13, -2)$ are located on a coordinate grid. Which measurement is closest to the distance between point A and point B?

A.   8 units   C.   15 units

B.   13 units   D.   17 units

18) Point A $(9,7)$ and point B $(4,-5)$ are located on a coordinate grid. Which measurement is closest to the distance between point A and point B?

   A. 8 units   C. 15 units

   B. 13 units   D. 17 units

19) In the xy-plane, the point $(-8,8)$ and $(4,-10)$ are on line A. Which of the following equations of lines is parallel to line A?

   A. $y = \frac{3}{2}x + 4$ C. $y = 2x + 4$

   B. $y = \frac{x}{2} - 3$ D. $y = -\frac{3}{2}x - 4$

20) What is the x-intercept of the line with equation $10x - 4y = 5$?

   A. -5 C. $\frac{1}{2}$

   B. -2 D. $\frac{5}{4}$

21) Giselle works as a carpenter and as a blacksmith. She earns \$20 as a carpenter and \$25 as a blacksmith. Last week, Giselle worked both jobs for a total of 30 hours and earned a total of \$690. How long did Giselle work as a carpenter last week, and how long did she work as a blacksmith?

   A. $(12, 20)$ C. $(12, 18)$

   B. $(10, 18)$ D. $(14, 16)$

22) Which of the following values for x and y satisfy the following system of equations?

$$\begin{cases} 3x + y = 8 \\ -5x - 2y = 0 \end{cases}$$

A. $x = 16, y = 20$

C. $x = 12, y = 40$

B. $x = -16, y = 35$

D. $x = 16, y = -40$

23) A ride in a taxicab costs \$1.25 for the first mile and \$1.15 for each additional mile. Which of the following could be used to calculate the total cost y of a ride that was x miles?

A. $x = 1.25(y - 1) + 1.15$

C. $y = 1.25(x - 1) + 1.15$

B. $x = 1.15(y - 1) + 1.25$

D. $y = 1.15(x - 1) + 1.25$

24) A caterer charges \$120 to cater a party for 15 people and \$200 for 25 people. Assume that the cost, y, is a linear function of the number of x people. Write an equation in slope-intercept form for this function. What does the slope represent? How much would a party for 40 people cost?

A. \$280

C. \$300

B. \$330

D. \$320

25) An attorney charges a fixed fee on \$250 for an initial meeting and \$150 per hour for all hours worked after that. Write a linear equation representation of the cost of hiring this attorney. Find the charge for 25 hours of work.

A. \$4000.00

C. \$3800.00

B. \$4200.00

D. \$4600.00

26) The sum of two numbers is 30. One of the numbers exceeds the other by 8. Find the numbers.

A. 9,15   C. 10,18

B. 12,20   D. 11,19

27) How is this number written in scientific notation?

$$0.0000005823$$

A. 0.5823×10^{-10} C. 5.823×10^{-7}

B. 5.823×10^{-6} D. 58.23×10^{-5}

28) How is this number written in scientific notation?

$$28{,}000{,}000{,}000$$

A. 2.8×10^{9} C. 28×10^{12}

B. 2.8×10^{10} D. 2.8×10^{8}

29) Calculate the area shaded region.

A: $2950mm^2$

B: $2940mm^2$

C: $3000mm^2$

D: $2930mm^2$

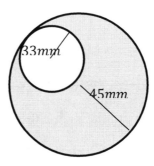

30) A circle is graphed on a coordinate grid and then reflected across the y-axis. If the center of the circle was located at (x, y), which ordered pair represents the new center after the transformation?

A. (x, y) C. $(-x, y)$

B. $(x, -y)$ D. $(-x, -y)$

31) Jason built a rectangular tool shed that is 9 meters wide and has an area of 117 square meters. What is the length of Jason's tool shed?

A. 10   C. 13

B. 14   D. 11

32) What is the estimated area of the shaded region?

A. $11cm^2$ C. $153cm^2$

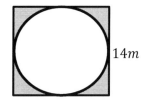

B. $42cm^2$ D. $196cm^2$

33) The Jackson Library is ordering some bookshelves. If x is the number of bookshelves the library wants to order, which each costs $100 and there is a one-time delivery charge of $800, which of the following represents the total cost, in dollar, per bookshelf?

A. $100x + 800$ C. $\frac{100x + 800}{100}$

B. $100 + 800x$ D. $\frac{100x + 800}{x}$

34) What is the median of these numbers?

32,33,65,12,45,95,82,65,48,72

A. 57   C. 55

B. 58   D. 56.5

35) What is the median of these numbers?1,3,9,5,11,15,26,14,18

A. 12   C. 14

B. 11   D. 10

36) What is the product of all possible values of x in the following equation?$|-3x + 4| = 26$

A. 12   C.11

B.9   D. 10

37) Out of 7 consonants and 4 vowels, how many words of 3 consonants and 2 vowels can be formed?

A. 24,400   C. 21,300

B. 21,000   D. 25,200

38) What is area of the figure?

A. 112.5

C. 115

B. 110

D. 112

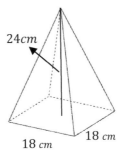

39) Find Volume of Pyramid?

A. 2,592 cm³

B. 2,682 cm³

C. 2,590 cm³

D. 2,400 cm³

40) 25 buses are running between two places P and Q. In how many ways can a person go from P to Q and return by a different bus?

A. 500

C. 610

B. 620

D. 600

This is the end of Practice Test 1

MCAS Math Practice Test 2

Grade 8

Mathematics

2019

1) Write the equation of a line with a slope of 5 and a y-intercept of $(0, -7)$.

   A: $y = 5x - 7$ C: $y = 4x - 7$

   B: $y = 5x - 4$ D: $y = 5x - 6$

2) A shirt costing \$350 is discounted 15%. After a month, the shirt is discounted another 10%. Which of the following expressions can be used to find the selling price of the shirt?

   A. $(350)(0.75)$ C. $(350)(0.15) - (350)(0.15)$

   B. $(350) - 350(0.25)$ D. $(350)(0.85)(0.90)$

3) When a number is subtracted from 32 and the difference is divided by that number, the result is 7. What is the value of the number?

   A. 6   C. 4

   B. 2   D. 3

4) John traveled 240 km in 6 hours and Alice traveled 120 km in 4 hours. What is the ratio of the average speed of John to average speed of Alice?

   A. $4:3$ C. $6:4$

   B. $3:4$ D. $5:3$

5) A ladder 10m long rests against a vertical wall. If the foot of the ladder is 6m away from the wall and the ladder just reaches the top of the wall, how high is the wall?

   A. $10m$ C. $6m$

   B. $8m$ D. $4m$

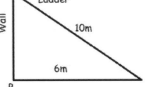

6) The low temperature in Anchorage, Alaska today was -4°F. The low temperature in Los Angeles, California was 63°F. What is the difference in the two low temperatures?

A. 59°

C. 57°

B. 67°

D. 14°

7) If 52% of a class are girls, and 30% of girls play tennis, what percent of the class play tennis?

A. 15.6%

C. 12.5%

B. 16.4%

D. 16%

8) The price of a car was $32,000 in 2014, $24,000 in 2015 and $18,000 in 2016. What is the rate of depreciation of the price of car per year?

A. 20%

C. 24%

B. 30%

D. 25%

9) A bag contains 6 red, 12 blue, 10 purple, and 4 orange marbles. One marble is selected at random. What is the probability that the marble chosen is blue?

A. $\frac{4}{13}$

C. $\frac{3}{16}$

B. $\frac{3}{8}$

D. $\frac{3}{5}$

10) The operator of an amusement park game kept track of how many tries it took participants to win the game. The following is the data from the first ten people:4,7,4,6,5,5,8,9,3,4. What is the median number of tries it took these participants to win the game?

   A. 8   C. 4

   B. 6   D. 5

11) Write 9.5×10^4 in decimal notation.

   A. 95,0000   C. 95,000

   B. 95,000   D. 0.00095

12) Jason and Bob are taking a $8\frac{3}{4}$ mile walk. If they walk at an average speed of $3\frac{1}{2}$ miles per hour, how long will it take them?

   A. $2\frac{2}{3}$ hours   C. $2\frac{1}{2}$ hours

   B. $30\frac{1}{8}$ hours   D. 5 hours

13) The width of a box is two third of its length. The height of the box is one fourth of its width. If the length of the box is 24 cm, what is the volume of the box?

   A. 1536   C. 1524

   B. 1546   D. 1527

14) If 45 % of A is 60 % of B, then B is what percent of A?

  A. 80%   C. 85%

  B. 133.33%   D. 125.5%

15) Mr. Reynolds owns $1\frac{3}{4}$ acres of land. He plans to buy the property next to his, which is $2\frac{3}{4}$ acres. How many acres will Mr. Reynolds own after the purchase?

  A. $5\frac{1}{4}$ C. $3\frac{1}{2}$

  B. $3\frac{3}{4}$ D. $4\frac{1}{2}$

16) In five successive hours, a car travels 25 km, 35 km, 30 km, 45 km and 50 km. In the next five hours, it travels with an average speed of 55 km per hour. Find the total distance the car traveled in 10 hours.

  A. 475   C. 460

  B. 490   D. 480

17) Where $\frac{3}{7} = \frac{x}{42}$, what is the value of x?

  A. 21   C. 7

  B. 6   D. 18

18) Rob purchased picnic food for $44.28 to share with three of his friends. They plan to split the cost evenly between the four friends. How much does each person need to pay Rob?

  A. $8.05   C. $7.26

  B. $8.30   D. $11.07

19) Hanna's sales goal for the week is $5,600. So far, she has sold $3,874.88 worth of merchandise. How much more does she need to sell to meet her goal?

   A. $1,725.38   C. $2,574.38

   B. $1,729.40   D. $1,725.12

20) What is the perimeter of a square in centimeters that has an area of 3969 cm²?

   Write your answer in the box below. (don't write the measurement)

   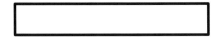

21) Find the area of a circle with a radius of 6 inches. The formula for the area of a circle is $A = \pi r^2$. Use 3.14 for π.

   A. 37.68 square inches   C. 9.42 square inches

   B. 113.04 square inches   D. 75.36 square inches

22) Mr. Carlos family are choosing a menu for their reception. They have 2 choices of appetizers, 6 choices of entrees, 3 choices of cake. How many different menu combinations are possible for them to choose?

   A. 28   C. 38

   B. 36   D. 34

23) The base side of a triangle is $2x + 1$ and height of that is $3x - 1$. What is the area of triangle?

   A. $6x^2 + x - 1$ C. $3x^2 + x - 1$

   B. $3x^2 + 0.5x - 0.5$ D. $6x^2 + 0.5x + 1$

24) 600 girls were surveyed about their favorite sport, 22% said that basketball is their favorite sport, 17% said that ice hockey is their favorite sport, and 35% said that softball is their favorite sport. The remaining girls said that field hockey is their favorite sport. How many of the girls surveyed said that field hockey is their favorite sport?

A. 150

B. 155

C. 156

D. 160

25) What is the value of x in the following system of equations?

$$\begin{cases} 3x - 6y = 0 \\ x + 3y = 4 \end{cases}$$

A. $\left(\frac{8}{5}, \frac{4}{5}\right)$

B. $\left(\frac{6}{5}, \frac{2}{5}\right)$

C. $(2,3)$

D. $\left(-\frac{8}{5}, -\frac{6}{5}\right)$

26) The diagonal of a rectangle is 15 inches long and the height of the rectangle is 12 inches. What is the perimeter of the rectangle in inches?

A. 40

B. 44

C. 42

D. 45

27) The ratio of boys and girls in a class is $6\!:\!8$. If there are 70 students in the class, how many more boys should be enrolled to make the ratio $1\!:\!1$?

A. 12

B. 10

C. 14

D. 8

28) Simplify $3x^3y^2z(2x^2yz)^3 =$

A. $6x^9y^5z^4$

C. $12x^9y^5z^2$

B. $24x^9y^5z^4$

D. $6x^8y^5z^4$

29) The square of a number is $\frac{81}{144}$. What is the cube of that number?

A. $\frac{512}{1728}$

C. $\frac{729}{1728}$

B. $\frac{343}{1728}$

D. $\frac{729}{1331}$

30) Nine minus five times a number, x, is no less than 39. Which of the following expressions represents all the possible values of the number?

A. $x \leq 6$

C. $x \leq -6$

B. $x \geq -6$

D. $x \geq 6$

31) A telephone company charges $.35 for the first minute of a phone call and $.15 for each additional minute of the call. Which of the following represents the cost y of a phone call lasting x minutes?

A. $y = 0.15(x - 1) + 0.35$

C. $y = 0.15x + 0.35$

B. $x = 0.15(y - 1) + 0.35$

D. $x = 0.15y + 0.35$

32) If 120 % of a number is 90, then what is the 80 % of that number?

A. 55

C. 70

B. 64

D. 60

33) The length of Kara's rectangular patio can be expressed as $3x - 2$ and the width can be expressed as $2x - 6$. In terms of x, what is the area of her patio?

A. $6x^2 + 13x - 6$ C. $6x^2 - 22x + 12$

B. $6x^2 - 12$ D. $2x^2 + 11x - 12$

34) From last year, the price of gasoline has increased from $1.20 per gallon to $1.65 per gallon. The new price is what percent of the original price?

A. 135   C. 137.5

B. 130   D. 140

35) A circular print is being matted in a square frame. If the frame is 18.5in by 18.5in, and the radius of the print is 8in, what is the area that not matted? (π=3.14)

A. $140.25 \, in^2$ C. $141.29 in^2$

B. $155.56 \, in^2$ D. $145.25 in^2$

36) A surveyor is hired to measure the distance of the opening of a bay. Using the illustration and various measurements determined on land, find the distance of the opening of the bay.

A. $62 \, yds$ C. $67.5 \, yds$

B. $57 \, yds$ D. $70 \, yds$

37) The circle graph below shows all Mr. Green's expenses for last month. If he spent $550 on his car, how much did he spend for his rent?

A. 675

B. 650

C. 700

D. 680

Mr. Green's monthly expenses

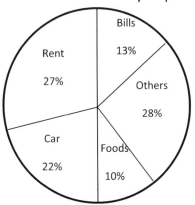

38) The radius of the following cylinder is 11 inches and its height is 23 inches. What is the surface area of the cylinder in square inches?

Write your answer in the box below. ($\pi = 3.14$)

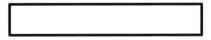

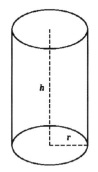

39) What is the value of the expression $2(2x - y) + (y - 2x)^2$ when $x = 2$ and $y = -4$?

A. 32

C. 0

B. 50

D. 80

40) Simplify the expression. $(6x^5 - 8x^2 + 2x^4) - (4x^2 + 3x^4 + 2x^5)$

A. $-4x^5 + 5x^4 - 11x^2$

C. $4x^5 - x^4 - 11x^2$

B. $4x^5 + x^4 + 11x^2$

D. $10x^5 + 5x^4 - 11x^2$

This is the end of Practice Test 2

MCAS Practice Tests Answers and Explanations

MCAS Math Practice Test 1				MCAS Math Practice Test 2			
1	C	21	C	1	A	21	B
2	$5\frac{7}{10}$	22	D	2	D	22	B
3	A	23	D	3	C	23	B
4	-37	24	D	4	A	24	C
5	768	25	A	5	B	25	A
6	C	26	D	6	B	26	C
7	D	27	C	7	A	27	B
8	C	28	B	8	D	28	B
9	60	29	B	9	B	29	C
10	C	30	C	10	D	30	C
11	B	31	C	11	B	31	C
12	D	32	B	12	C	32	D
13	D	33	B	13	A	33	C
14	C	34	D	14	B	34	D
15	B	35	B	15	D	35	C
16	B	36	D	16	C	36	B
17	D	37	D	17	D	37	A
18	B	38	A	18	D	38	1,921.68
19	D	39	A	19	D	39	D
20	C	40	D	20	252	40	C

MCAS Practice Test 1 Explanations

1) Choice C is correct

Jason ate $\frac{1}{2}$ of 8 parts of his pizza. It means 4 parts out of 8 parts ($\frac{1}{2}$ of 8 parts is $x \Rightarrow x = 4$) and left 4 parts. Eva ate $\frac{3}{4}$ of 8 parts of her pizza. It means 6 parts out of 8 parts ($\frac{3}{4}$ of 8 parts is $x \Rightarrow x = 6$) and left 2 parts.

Therefore, they ate $(4 + 6)$ parts out of $(8 + 8)$ parts of their pizza and left $(4 + 2)$ parts out of $(8 + 8)$ parts of their pizza that equals to: $\frac{6}{16}$

After simplification, the answer is: $\frac{3}{8}$

2) The answer is $5\frac{7}{10}$ miles.

Robert runs $3\frac{1}{10}$ miles on Saturday and $2 \times (3\frac{1}{10})$ miles on Monday and Wednesday. Robert wants to run a total of 18 miles this week.

Therefore: $3\frac{1}{10} + 2 \times (3\frac{1}{10})$ should be subtracted from 18:

$18 - \left(3\frac{1}{10} + 2\left(3\frac{1}{10}\right)\right) = 15 - 9\frac{3}{10} = 5\frac{7}{10}$ miles.

3) Choice A is correct

Let x be the integer. Then: $2x + 20 = 68$. Subtract 20 both sides: $2x = 48$. Divide both sides by $2 \Rightarrow x = 24$

4) The answer is: -37

Use PEMDAS (order of operation):

$[3 \times (-21) + (5 \times 2)] - (-25) + [(-3) \times 6] \div 2 = [-63 + 10] + 25 + [-18] \div 2$
$$= -53 + 25 - 9 = -37$$

5) The answer is 768 cm.

Write the proportion and solve for missing side.

$$\frac{\text{Smaller triangle height}}{\text{Smaller triangle base}} = \frac{\text{Bigger triangle height}}{\text{Bigger triangle base}} \Rightarrow \frac{100cm}{160cm} = \frac{100+380cm}{x} \Rightarrow x = 768cm$$

6) Choice C is correct.

Write the proportion and solve. $\frac{3ft}{2ft} = \frac{x}{38ft} \Rightarrow x = 57\,ft$

7) Choice D is correct.

The distance that Mike runs can be found by the following equation:

$D_M = 5.5t + 7.5$. The distance Julia runs can be found by $D_J = 8t$

Julia catches Mike if they run the same distance. Therefore:

$8t = 5.5t + 7.5 \Rightarrow 2.5t = 7.5 \Rightarrow t = \frac{7.5}{2.5} = 3\ hours$

8) Choice C is correct

x is the number of all sales profit and 2%of it is:

$2\% \times x = 0.02x$. Employer's revenue: $0.2x + 7{,}000$

9) The answer is 60.

Jason needs an 75% average to pass the exams. Therefore, the sum of 5 exams must be at least $5 \times 75 = 375$. The sum of 4 exams is: $68 + 72 + 85 + 90 = 315$. The minimum score Jason can earn on final test to pass is: $375 - 315 = 60$

10) Choice C is correct.

We can write: $\frac{25}{100} = \frac{8}{x} \Rightarrow \frac{8 \times 100}{25} = x \Rightarrow x = 32$

11) Choice B is correct.

Let x be the amount of angle and y be the amount of its supplement. The angle and its supplement are 180° in total $(x + y = 180°)$. we have: $x = \frac{1}{5}y$

$x + y = \frac{1}{5}y + y = 180° \Rightarrow y = 150°$ and $x = 30°$

12) Choice D is correct

$y = x + 1 \Rightarrow$ if $x = 0$ therefore $y = 1$ and if $y = 0$ therefore $x = -1$. Hence answer d is correct.

13) Choice D is correct

$\begin{cases} \frac{-x}{2} + \frac{y}{4} = 1 \\ \frac{-5y}{6} + 2x = 4 \end{cases} \Rightarrow$ Multiply the top equation by 4. Then,

$\begin{cases} -2x + y = 4 \\ \frac{-5y}{6} + 2x = 4 \end{cases} \Rightarrow$ Add two equations.

$\frac{1}{6}y = 8 \Rightarrow y = 48$, plug in the value of y into the first equation $\Rightarrow x = 22$

14) Choice C is correct

$\begin{cases} x + 4y = 10 \\ 5x + 10y = 20 \end{cases} \Rightarrow$ Multiply the top equation by -5 then,

$\begin{cases} -5x - 20y = -50 \\ 5x + 10y = 20 \end{cases} \Rightarrow$ Add two equations

$-10y = -30 \rightarrow y = 3$, plug in the value of y into the first equation

$x + 4y = 10 \Rightarrow x + 4(3) = 10 \Rightarrow x + 12 = 10$

Subtract 12 from both sides of the equation. Then: $x + 12 = 10 \rightarrow x = -2$

15) Choice B is correct.

$\frac{21 + 18 + 16 + x}{4} = 20 \Rightarrow \frac{55 + x}{4} = 20 \Rightarrow 55 + x = 80 \Rightarrow x = 25$

16) Choice B is correct.

Solve for x. $5 \le 3x - 1 < 11 \Rightarrow$ (add 1 all sides)

$5 + 1 \le 3x - 1 + 1 < 11 + 1 \Rightarrow 6 \le 3x < 12 \Rightarrow$ (divide all sides by 3)

$2 \le x < 4 \Rightarrow x$ is between 2 and 4.

17) Choice D is correct.

Distance between two points is equal: $\sqrt{(x_1-x_2)^2+(y_1-y_2)^2}$

18) Choice B is correct

Distance between two points is equal: $\sqrt{(x_1-x_2)^2+(y_1-y_2)^2}$
$\sqrt{(9-4)^2+(7-(-5)^2}=\sqrt{(5)^2+(12)^2}=\sqrt{169}=13$

19) Choice D is correct

The slop of line A is: $m=\frac{y_2-y_1}{x_2-x_1}=\frac{-10-8}{4-(-8)}=-\frac{3}{2}$
Also $(y-y_1)=m(x-x_1)\Rightarrow y-8=-\frac{3}{2}(x+8)\Rightarrow y=-\frac{3}{2}x-4$

20) Choice C is correct

The value of y in the x-intercept of a line is zero. Then:
$y=0\to 10x-4(0)=5\to 10x=5\to x=\frac{1}{2}$. Then, x-intercept of the line is $\frac{1}{2}$

21) Choice C is correct

The total amount of money Giselle made as a carpenter can be modeled by $20x$, and the total amount of money she made as a blacksmith can be modeled by $25y$. Since these together add up to $690, we get the following equation:
$20x+25y=690$.
We are also given that last week, Giselle worked as a carpenter and a blacksmith for a total of 30 hours. This can be expressed as: $x+y=30\Rightarrow y=30-x$
Therefor $20x+25(30-x)=690\Rightarrow x=12\ and\ y=18$

22) Choice D is correct

$\begin{cases}3x+y=8\\-5x-2y=0\end{cases}\Rightarrow$ Multiply the top equation by 2 then,
$\begin{cases}6x+2y=16\\-5x-2y=0\end{cases}\Rightarrow$ Add two equations
$x=16$, plug in the value of y into the first equation
$3x+y=8\to 3(16)+y=8\to y=-40$

23) Choice D is correct

Let $x=$ the total miles of the ride.
Therefore, $x-1=$ the additional miles of the ride. The correct equation takes $1.25 and adds it to $1.15 times the number of additional miles, $x-1$. Translating, this becomes: $y(the\ total\ cost)=1.25+1.15(x-1)$, which is the same equation as $y=1.15(x-1)+1.25$.

24) Choice D is correct.

Write as two points in terms of: (number of people, cost in$) (15,120) and (25,200). Find the equation of the line using: $m=\frac{y2-y1}{x2-x1}$ and $y=mx+b$
Equation: $Y=8x$ plug in $x=40$, $y=8(40)=320$. A party of 40 people will cost $320.00.

25) Choice A is correct

$C = 250 + 150h$. Assuming the initial meeting counts for the 1st hour, you would plug in $h = 25$ for a total cost of $4000.00.

26) Choice D is correct

Let the number be x. Then the other number$= x + 8$. Sum of two numbers$= 30$. According to question, $x + x + 8 = 30 \Rightarrow 2x + 8 = 30 \Rightarrow 2x = 22 \Rightarrow x = 11$. Therefore, $x + 8 = 11 + 8 = 19$

27) Choice C is correct.

$$0.0000005823 = 5.823 \times 10^{-7}$$

28) Choice B is correct.

$$28{,}000{,}000{,}000 = 2.8 \times 10^{10}$$

29) Choice B is correct.

The area of greater circle is: $A_g = \pi r^2 = \pi . (45)^2 = 6361.7 mm^2$

The area of smaller circle is: $A_s = \pi r^2 = \pi . (33)^2 = 3421.2 mm^2$

Then area of colored part is $A_c = A_g - A_s = 6361.7 - 3421.2 = 2940.5 mm^2$

30) Choice C is correct.

When a point is reflected over y axes, the (x) coordinate of that point changes to $(-x)$, while its y coordinate remains the same.

31) Choice C is correct.

Use $A_{reg} = l \times w \Rightarrow 117 = l \times 9$. We can solve for the length by dividing.

$l = \frac{117}{9} = 13$

32) Choice B is correct.

To estimate area of the shaded region, subtract area of the circle from area of the square. The area of the square formula: $S = a2$ and the area of circle formula: $S = \pi r^2$ Therefore $S_{square} - S_{circle} = a^2 - \pi r^2 \Rightarrow$

$S_{square} - S_{circle} = (14)^2 - \pi(\frac{14}{2})^2 \Rightarrow S_{square} - S_{circle} = 42\ cm^2$

33) Choice B is correct.

The amount of money for x bookshelf is: $100x$

Then, the total cost of all bookshelves is equal to: $100x + 800$

The total cost, in dollar, per bookshelf is: $\frac{Total\ cost}{number\ of\ items} = \frac{100x + 800}{x}$

34) Choice D is correct.

The median of the numbers is the number in the middle. First write the numbers in order from least to greatest. $12, 32, 33, 45, 48, 65, 65, 72, 82, 95$

Since the number of numbers is even, we need to find the average of two numbers in the middle. $48 + 65 = 113 \rightarrow \frac{113}{2} = 56.5$

35) Choice B is correct.

Write the numbers in order: 1, 3, 5, 9, 11, 14, 15, 18, 26. The median is the number in the middle, which is 11.

36) Choice D is correct

To solve absolute values equations, write two equations. $|-3x + 4| = 26$ can equal positive 26, or negative 26. Therefore $-3x + 4 = 26 \Rightarrow x = \frac{22}{-3}$ and $-3x + 4 = -26 \Rightarrow x = \frac{-26-4}{-3} = 10$

37) The answer is D.

Number of ways of selecting 3 consonants from 7 is $7C3$
Number of ways of selecting 2 vowels from 4 is $4C2$
Number of ways of selecting 3 consonants from 7 and 2 vowels from 4 is
$^7C_3 \times {}^4C_2 = \left(\frac{7 \times 6 \times 5}{3 \times 2 \times 1}\right) \times \left(\frac{4 \times 3}{2 \times 1}\right) = 210$
It means we can have 210 groups where each group contains total 5 letters (3 consonants and 2 vowels). Number of ways of arranging 5 letters among themselves= $5! = 120$ Hence, required number of ways= $210 \times 120 = 25,200$

38) Choice A is correct

The area of Trapezoids is $\frac{(a+b).h}{2} \Rightarrow A = \frac{(10+15)9}{2} = 112.5$

39) Choice A is correct

Volume of pyramid is equal to $\frac{1}{3}(base\ edge)^2(height) \Rightarrow$
$$V = \frac{1}{3} \times (18)^2 \times 24 = 2592 cm^3$$

40) Choice D is correct

He can go in any of the 25 buses (25 ways). Since he cannot come back in the same bus, he can return in 24 ways. Total number of ways $= 25 \times 24 = 600$

MCAS Practice Test 2 Explanations

1) Choice A is correct.

Since $m = 5$ and $(0, -7)$ is the y-intercept, $b = -7$, then substituting into the form $y = mx + b$ will give us the equation of the line: $y = 5x - 7$

2) Choice D is correct.

To find the discount, multiply the number by $(100\% - rate\ of\ discount)$.

Therefore, for the first discount we get:

$(350) (100\% - 15\%) = (350) (0.85)$

For the next 10 % discount: $(350) (0.85) (0.90)$

3) Choice C is correct.

Let x be the number. Write the equation and solve for x. $(32 - x) \div x = 7$

Multiply both sides by x. $(32 - x) = 7x$, then add x both sides. $32 = 8x$, now divide both sides by 8. $x = 4$

4) Choice A is correct.

The average speed of john is: $240 \div 6 = 40$ km

The average speed of Alice is: $120 \div 4 = 30$ km

Write the ratio and simplify. $40:30 \Rightarrow 4:3$

5) Choice B is correct.

Let AC be the ladder. Therefore, $AC = 10m$
Let BC be the distance between the foot of the ladder and the wall.
Therefore, $BC = 6m$
$\triangle ABC$ forms a right-angled triangle, right angled at B.
By Pythagoras theorem, $AC^2 = AB^2 + BC^2 \Rightarrow 100 = AB^2 + 36$ Or
$AB^2 = 100 - 36 = 100 - 36 = 64$ Or $AB = \sqrt{64} = 8m$. Hence, the wall is $8m$ high.

6) Choice B is correct.

Visualize a number line. The distance from (-4) to 0 is 4. Then, the distance from 0 to 63 is 63. Add the two distances together to get 67. $63 + 4 = 67$.

7) Choice A is correct.

The percent of girls playing tennis is:

$52\% \times 30\% = 0.52 \times 0.30 = 0.156 = 15.6\%$

8) Choice D is correct.

Use this formula: Percent of Change: $\frac{\text{New Value} - \text{Old Value}}{\text{Old Value}} \times 100\%$

$\frac{24000 - 32000}{32000} \times 100\% = 25\%$ and $\frac{18000 - 24000}{24000} \times 100\% = 25\%$

9) Choice B is correct.

The probability of blue is $\frac{blue}{total}$. The number of blue marbles is 12, and the total number of marbles is 16 ($6 + 12 + 10 + 4 = 32$). Therefore, the probability of choosing a blue is $\frac{12}{32} = \frac{3}{8}$

10) Choice D is correct.

First, put the numbers in order from least to greatest, and then find the middle of the set. 4,7,4,6,5,5,8,9,3,4. The middle is the average (mean) of the 5th and 6th data items. The mean of 5 and 5 is 5.

11) Choice B is correct.

Move the decimal point 4 places to the right to get 95,000.

12) Choice C is correct.

To find the amount of time that it took Jason and Bob, divide the distance $8\frac{3}{4}$ by the rate $3\frac{1}{2}$. $8\frac{3}{4} \div 3\frac{1}{2} = \frac{35}{4} \div \frac{7}{2} = \frac{35}{4} \times \frac{2}{7} = 2\frac{1}{2}$

13) Choice A is correct.

If the length of the box is 24, then the width of the box is two third of it, 16, and the height of the box is 4 (one fourth of the width). The volume of the box is: $V = lwh = (24)(16)(4) = 1536$

14) Choice B is correct.

Write the equation and solve for B: $0.45A = 0.60B$, divide both sides by 0.60, then: $\frac{0.45 A}{0.60} = B$, therefore: $B = 0.75 A$, and B is 0.75 times of A or it's 133.33% of A.

15) Choice D is correct.

Add the two pieces of land together; $1\frac{3}{4} + 2\frac{3}{4} = 3\frac{3}{4}$. Add the whole numbers. Since the denominators are already the same, just add the numerators and keep the denominator the same; $\frac{6}{4}$ can be simplified to $1\frac{1}{2}$. Add this to the whole number to get $4\frac{1}{2}$ acres.

16) Choice C is correct.

Add the first 5 numbers. $25 + 35 + 30 + 45 + 50 = 185$

To find the distance traveled in the next 5 hours, multiply the average by number of hours. $Distance = Average \times Rate = 55 \times 5 = 275$, Add both numbers. $275 + 185 = 460$

17) Choice D is correct.

Determine what number 7 was multiplied by to get 42 and multiply the numerator by the same number. Seven was multiplied by six, so $3 \times 6 = 18$. The value of x is 18.

18) Choice D is correct.

You must divide the cost of the food by 4 to split the cost evenly among the four friends; $44.28 \div 4 = \$11.07$.

19) Choice D is correct.

You must find the difference (subtraction) between her goal and what she has already sold. Add a decimal and two zeros to the end of $5,600 ($5,600.00) to make the subtraction easier; $5,600.00 - \$3,874.88 = \$1,725.12$.

20) Answer is 252.

The area of the square is 3969. Therefore, the side of the square is square root of the area. $\sqrt{3969} = 63$. Four times the side of the square is the perimeter: $4 \times 63 = 252$

21) Choice B is correct.

Substitute 6 for r in the formula $A = \pi r^2$. $A = 3.14 \times 6^2 = 113.04$

22) Choice B is correct.

To find the number of possible outfit combinations, multiply number of options for each factor: $2 \times 6 \times 3 = 36$

23) Choice B is correct.

Area of triangle is: $\frac{b \times h}{2} \Rightarrow \frac{1}{2}(2x+1)(3x-1) = \frac{1}{2}(6x^2 + x - 1) \Rightarrow A = 3x^2 + 0.5x - 0.5$

24) Choice C is correct.

The percent must add up to 100%; $22\% + 17\% + 35\% = 74\%$. If 74% of the girls surveyed have been accounted for, the remainder of the girls must have said that field hockey is their favorite sport. To find the percent that said field hockey is their favorite sport, subtract 74% from 100%; $100\% - 74\% = 26\%$; The girls said that field hockey is their favorite sport is $0.26 \times 600 = 156$

25) Choice A is correct.

$3x - 6y = 0$
$x + 3y = 4$. Multiply the second equation by 2. then add it to the first equation.

$2(x + 3y = 4) \Rightarrow 2x + 6y = 8 \Rightarrow \begin{matrix} 3x - 6y = 0 \\ +2x + 6y = 8 \\ \hline 5x = 8 \end{matrix} \Rightarrow x = \frac{8}{5}. \ 3x - 6y = 0 \Rightarrow$

$\frac{24}{5} - 6y = 0 \Rightarrow 6y = \frac{24}{5} \Rightarrow y = \frac{4}{5}$

26) Choice C is correct.

Let x be the width of the rectangle. Use Pythagorean Theorem:

$a^2 + b^2 = c^2$

$x^2 + 12^2 = 15^2 \Rightarrow x^2 + 144 = 225 \Rightarrow x^2 = 225 - 144 = 81 \Rightarrow x = 9$

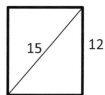

Perimeter of the rectangle $= 2(length + width) = 2(12 + 9) = 2(21) = 42$

27) Choice B is correct.

The ratio of boy to girls is 6:8. Therefore, there are 6 boys out of 14 students. To find the answer, first divide the total number of students by 14, then multiply the result by 6. $70 \div 14 = 5 \Rightarrow 5 \times 6 = 30$

There are 30 boys and 40(70−30) girls. So, 10 more boys should be enrolled to make the ratio 1:1

28) Choice B is correct.
29) Choice C is correct.

The square of a number is $\frac{81}{144}$, then the number is the square root of $\frac{81}{144}$

$\sqrt{\frac{81}{144}} = \frac{9}{12}$. The cube of the number is: $(\frac{9}{12})^3 = \frac{729}{1728}$

30) Choice C is correct.
31) Choice C is correct.

Let x = the total minutes of the call. Therefore, $x - 1$ = the additional minutes of the call. This choice is correct because in order to calculate the cost, the charge is 35 cents plus 15 cents times the number of additional minutes. If y represents the total cost, then y equals 0.35 plus 0.15 times the quantity $x - 1$. This translates to $y = 0.35 + 0.15(x - 1)$ or $y = 0.15(x - 1) + 0.35$.

32) Choice D is correct.

First, find the number. Let x be the number. Write the equation and solve for x.

120 % of a number is 90, then: $1.2 \times x = 90 \Rightarrow x = 90 \div 1.2 = 75$

80 % of 75 is: $\quad\quad\quad\quad 0.8 \times 75 = 60$

33) Choice C is correct.

The area of a square is weight x length.

$A = (3x - 2)(2x - 6) = 6x^2 - 22x + 12$

34) Choice C is correct.

The question is this: 1.65 is what percent of 1.20?

Use percent formula: part = $\frac{percent}{100} \times whole \Rightarrow 1.65 = \frac{percent}{100} \times 1.20 \Rightarrow 1.65 = \frac{percent \times 1.20}{100} \Rightarrow 165 = percent \times 1.20 \Rightarrow percent = \frac{165}{1.20} = 137.5$

35) Choice C is correct.

The area paper is $A_{sq} = 18.5 \times 18.5 = 342.25$ in². The area of circular matted on paper is $A_{matted} = \pi r^2 = 3.14 \times (8)^2 = 200.96$. thus the area of that not matted is $A_{sq} - A_{matted} = 342.25 - 200.96 = 141.29$

36) Choice B is correct.

$\triangle$ACE and $\triangle$BCD are similar triangles. Using this fact, the following proportion is true: $\frac{\overline{AC}}{\overline{AB}} = \frac{\overline{AE}}{\overline{BD}}$ or $\frac{190}{150} = \frac{x}{45} \Rightarrow x = 57$ yards.

37) Choice A is correct

Let x be all expenses, then $\frac{22}{100}x = \$550 \rightarrow x = \frac{100 \times \$550}{22} = \$2500$. He spent for his rent: $\frac{27}{100} \times \$2500 = \$675$

38) The answer is 1921.68.

Surface Area of a $cylinder = 2\pi r(r + h)$, The radius of the cylinder is 11 inches and its height is 23 inches. $\pi = 3.14$.

Therefore: $Surface\ Area\ of\ a\ cylinder = 2(3.14)(11)(11 + 23) = 1921.68$

39) Choice D is correct

$x = 2$ and $y = -4 \Rightarrow 2(2x - y) + (y - 2x)^2 = 2(4 + 4) + (-4 - 4)^2 = 16 + 64 = 80$

40) Choice C is correct

Simplify and combine like terms. $(6x^5 - 8x^2 + 2x^4) - (4x^2 + 3x^4 + 2x^5) = 4x^5 - x^4 - 11x^2$

www.EffortlessMath.com

... So Much More Online!

✓ FREE Math lessons

✓ More Math learning books!

✓ Mathematics Worksheets

✓ Online Math Tutors

Need a PDF version of this book?

Send email to: Info@EffortlessMath.com

Made in the USA
Middletown, DE
23 January 2023

22921974R00095